Everyday
Mathematics®

Home Links

Everyday Mathematics®

Home Links

**The University of Chicago
School Mathematics Project**

A Division of The McGraw·Hill Companies

*Columbus, Ohio
Chicago, Illinois*

UCSMP Elementary Materials Component

Max Bell, Director

Authors

Max Bell · Andy Isaacs*
Jean Bell · James McBride,
John Bretzlauf* ·   Director
Amy Dillard* · Kathleen Pitvorec*
Robert Hartfield · Peter Saecker

Technical Art

Diana Barrie*

Second Edition only

Contributors

Robert Balfanz, Judith Busse, Ellen Dairyko, Lynn Evans, James Flanders, Dorothy Freedman, Nancy Gile Goodsell, Pam Guastafeste, Nancy Harvey, Murray Hozinsky, Deborah Arron Leslie, Sue Lindsley, Mariana Mardus, Carol Montag, Elizabeth Moore, Kate Morrison, William D. Pattison, Joan Penderson, Brenda Penix, June Ploen, Herb Rice, Dannette Riehle, Ellen Ryan, Marie Schilling, Susan Sherill, Patricia Smith, Robert Strang, Janorida Strong, Kevin Sweeney, Sally Vongsathern, Esther Weiss, Francine Williams, Michael Wilson, Izaak Wirzup.

Photo Credits

Phil Martin/Photography, Jack Demuth/Photography, Cover Credits: Leaf, tomato, buttons/Bill Burlingham Photography, Tree rings background/Peter Samuels/Stone, Photo Collage: Herman Adler Design

Permissions

Math Masters Home Link 3.1, page 51:
Window Panes by Walter Neal/*Chicago Tribune*

Family Letter Home Link 6.13,
page 173 (middle center and middle right): Jack Demuth/Photography

www.sra4kids.com

SRA/McGraw-Hill

A Division of The McGraw-Hill Companies

Send all inquiries to:
SRA/McGraw-Hill
P.O. Box 812960
Chicago, IL 60681

Printed in the United States of America.

ISBN 1-57039-944-1

12 13 14 15 16 17 18 19 20 WAL 08 07 06 05

Contents

Family Letter

Introduction to First Grade Everyday Mathematics

Welcome to *First Grade Everyday Mathematics*. It is part of an elementary school mathematics curriculum developed by the University of Chicago School Mathematics Project (UCSMP). *Everyday Mathematics* offers children a broad background in mathematics.

Several features of the program are described below to help familiarize you with the structure and expectations of *Everyday Mathematics*.

A problem-solving approach based on everyday situations. By making connections between their own knowledge and their experiences in school and outside of school, children learn basic skills in meaningful contexts so that mathematics becomes "real."

Frequent practice of basic skills. Instead of practice presented in a single, tedious drill format, children practice basic skills in a variety of engaging ways. In addition to completing daily mixed review pages, patterning on the number grid, and working with addition and subtraction fact families in different formats, children will play games that are specifically designed to develop basic skills.

An instructional approach that revisits concepts regularly. To enhance the development of basic skills and concepts, children regularly revisit previously learned concepts and repeatedly practice skills encountered earlier. The lessons are designed to take advantage of previously learned concepts and skills and to build on them throughout the year instead of treating them as isolated bits of knowledge.

A curriculum that explores mathematical content beyond basic arithmetic. Mathematics standards in the United States, as well as around the world, indicate that basic arithmetic skills are only the beginning of the mathematical knowledge children will need as they develop critical thinking skills. In addition to basic arithmetic, *Everyday Mathematics* develops concepts and skills in the following topics—numeration; operations and computation; data and chance; geometry; measurement and reference frames; and patterns, functions, and algebra.

First Grade Everyday Mathematics emphasizes the following content:

- **Numeration** Counting; reading and writing numbers; investigating place value of whole numbers; exploring fractions and money.

- **Operations and Computation** Learning addition and subtraction facts, fact families, and extended facts; beginning informal work with properties of numbers and problem solving.

- **Data and Chance** Collecting, organizing, and displaying data using tables, charts, and graphs.

- **Geometry** Exploring 2- and 3-dimensional shapes.

- **Measurement and Reference Frames** Using tools to measure length, capacity (quarts, liters), and weight; using clocks, calendars, timelines, thermometers, and ordinal numbers.

- **Patterns, Functions, and Algebra** Exploring attributes, patterns, sequences, relations, and functions; finding missing numbers and rules in Frames-and-Arrows and "What's My Rule?" problems; studying properties of operations.

Everyday Mathematics will provide you with ample opportunities to monitor your child's progress and to participate in your child's mathematics experiences.

Throughout the year, you will receive Family Letters to keep you informed of the mathematical content your child will be studying in each unit. Each letter will include a vocabulary list, suggested *Do-Anytime Activities* for you and your child, and an answer guide to selected Home Link (homework) activities.

You will enjoy seeing your child's confidence and comprehension soar as he or she connects mathematics to everyday life.

We look forward to an exciting year!

Use with Lesson 1.1.

Unit 1: Establishing Routines

One purpose of this first unit is to help children become comfortable with a cooperative-learning environment while building mathematical concepts. Another purpose is to introduce and establish routines that will be used throughout this year and in the grades to come. This unit also reviews various mathematical concepts that were introduced in Kindergarten.

In Unit 1, children will review counting by 1s, 2s, 5s, and 10s. They will have opportunities to count and record numbers of various objects, such as hands, fingers, eyes, and ears. In addition, they will use pennies to count money, practice writing numbers, and begin to use a thermometer.

Vocabulary

Important terms in Unit 1:

Home Links Activities intended to promote follow-up and enrichment experiences at home. Each Home Link activity is identified by the following symbol:

tally count Marks used to keep track of an amount counted or other data collected over a period of time. Tallies serve as a model for children to represent numbers they can count and say but cannot yet write.

HHT /// is the tally count
for the number 8.

temperature scales Columns of numbers found on thermometers. Most thermometers have both a Fahrenheit scale and a Celsius scale.

tool kits Individual zippered bags or boxes used in the classroom. They contain a variety of items, such as rulers, pennies, and number cards, to help children understand mathematical ideas.

Do-Anytime Activities

To work with your child on concepts taught in this unit, try these interesting and rewarding activities:

1 Count orally by 2s, 5s, and 10s when doing chores, riding in the car, or shopping at the grocery store. Occasionally count down, or back; for example: 90, 80, 70, 60, ...

2 Take inventories around the house and while shopping, and have your child keep track of each count using tally marks.

For example, count food items and nonfood items bought at the grocery store:

|||| |||| |||| | |||| ||

food items   nonfood items

3 Listen to and discuss weather reports with your child.

As You Help Your Child with Homework

As your child brings home assignments, you may want to go over the instructions together, clarifying them as necessary. The answers listed below will guide you through this unit's Home Links.

Home Link 1.9

Other possible answers include: TV listings, food packages (expiration dates), and clocks.

Home Link 1.12

Other possible answers include: oven, refrigerator, freezer, and thermostat.

Home Link 1.13

Sample number story: There are 5 flowers in the garden. If I pick 1 of them to give to my teacher, how many flowers will be left? 4

NOTE: Encourage your child to come up with his or her own way to solve the problem, whether it's thinking logically, drawing pictures, or counting on fingers. As an adult, you know that $5 - 4 = 1$, but for your child, coming up with his or her own strategy is more natural than thinking of the number story as $5 - 4 = 1$.

4

Use with Lesson 1.1.

Name _____ Date _____

Numbers Are Everywhere

**Family
Note**

In *First Grade Everyday Mathematics*, children "do mathematics." We expect that children will want to share their enthusiasm for mathematics activities with members of their families. Therefore, your child will bring home assignments and activities throughout the year. These assignments, called "Home Links," will be identified by the symbol in the upper right-hand corner of this page. The assignments will not take very much time to complete, but most of them involve interaction with an adult or an older child.

There are good reasons for including Home Links in the first grade program:
· The assignments encourage children to take initiative and responsibility for completing them. As you respond with encouragement and assistance, you help your child build independence and self-confidence.

· Home Links reinforce newly learned skills and concepts. They provide thinking and practice time at each child's own pace.

· These assignments are often designed to relate what is done in school to children's lives outside school. This helps tie mathematics to the real world, which is very important in the *Everyday Mathematics* program.

· Home Links will give you a better idea of what mathematics your child is learning.

Generally, you can help by listening and responding to your child's requests and comments about mathematics. You can also help by linking·numbers to real life, pointing out ways in which you use numbers (time, TV channels, page numbers, telephone numbers, bus routes, shopping lists, and so on). Extending the notion that "children who have someone read to them learn to read," *Everyday Mathematics* supports the belief that children who have someone do math with them, learn math. Playful counting and thinking games that are fun for both you and your child are very helpful for such learning.

For this first Home Link, your child might look for a newspaper ad for grocery items, a calendar page, or a picture of a clock. The purpose of this activity is to expand your child's awareness of numbers in the everyday world.

Please return this Home Link to school tomorrow.

Collect examples of numbers.
Paste some examples on the back of this page.

Bring examples that will not fit on this page to school.
Do not bring anything valuable or breakable!

Calendars

Family Note

Children might find dates on items like the following: watches, VCRs, newspapers, magazines, and mail with canceled stamps.

   Every few days, ask your child to look at a calendar and tell you that day's date. We are just beginning to record counts with tallies. Remind your child how to show 5: Make four tallies "standing tall" and then make the fifth mark across the 4 tallies, as follows: ////

Please return this Home Link to school tomorrow.

What do you think of when you hear the word *date*?

Ask someone in your home to write what she or he thinks *date* means.

Date means _____

_____

_____

Look for calendars in your home. Have someone help you. Make a tally count of the number of calendars you find.

Count your total tally marks.

I found _____ calendars.

Can you find other things with dates on them?

Draw pictures of them on the back of this page.

Tally Marks

Family Note

Remind your child that the fifth tally mark crosses the other four, as follows: Ⳙⵤ
Counting on is an important skill that children practice whenever they count tally marks. Check that your child first counts by 5s for the groups of 5 tallies and then counts by 1s. For example, Ⳙⵤ Ⳙⵤ Ⳙⵤ /// should be counted as 5, 10, 15, 16, 17, 18. Developing this skill will take some practice.

Please return this Home Link to school tomorrow.

Write 5 numbers. Make tally marks for each number.

Number	Tally Marks
18	Ⳙⵤ Ⳙⵤ Ⳙⵤ ///

Family Note

Time is set aside regularly in *First Grade Everyday Mathematics* for Exploration activities that involve children in data collecting, problem solving, familiarization with math manipulatives, and games in independent and small-group settings. Children will have the opportunity to participate in several activities during each Exploration session. Please ask your child about our class's mathematics Explorations.

Please return this Home Link to school tomorrow.

Tell someone at home about your favorite mathematics Exploration. Draw something you did in your Explorations today.

Thermometers

Family Note

Objects that show temperatures might be kitchen items (such as a meat thermometer) or health care items (such as a heating pad). These items do not need to show degrees Fahrenheit—they may have their own temperature gauges showing levels of heat or cold.

Please return this Home Link to school tomorrow.

1. Look for thermometers in your home.

I found _____ thermometers in my home.

2. Do a temperature hunt. Ask someone at home to help you find other things that show temperatures.

   a. Draw some of the things you find.

   b. Write the name for each of your drawings.

   Have someone at home help you.

Number Stories

Family Note

"Number story" is another name for what is traditionally called a "story problem" or a "word problem." *Everyday Mathematics* uses the term "number story" to emphasize the fact that the story must involve numbers.

Please return this Home Link to school tomorrow.

1. Find a picture of a group of things, such as animals, people, flowers, or toys.

Have someone at home help you.

2. Tell a number story about your picture to someone at home.

3. Then glue or tape your picture to this page.

Unit 2: Everyday Uses of Numbers

In Unit 2, children will learn about three specific uses of numbers in real-world contexts: the use of numbers in telephone numbers, in telling time, and in counting money. Your child will learn how to interpret the various parts of a telephone number (the area code, the prefix, and the last four digits), how to tell time on the hour, and how to count collections of nickels and pennies.

When learning to tell time, your child will estimate the time on a clock that has no minute hand, only an hour hand. For example, when the hour hand is pointing exactly to the 4, we can say that the time is *about 4 o'clock*. When the hour hand is between the 4 and the 5, we can say that the time is *after 4 o'clock* or *between 4 and 5 o'clock*. By focusing on the hour hand, children will avoid the common mistake of giving the wrong hour reading (usually one hour off).

about 4 o'clock   between 4 o'clock and 5 o'clock

When learning to count money, it is preferred that your child use real coins. In Unit 2, the focus will be on counting nickels and pennies and on exchanging pennies for nickels. (In Unit 3, children will add dimes to their coin collections. Later on, they will add quarters.)

Your child will also continue to develop counting skills with the help of a number grid, begin to do simple addition and subtraction problems, and continue to solve number stories.

Please keep this letter for reference as your child works through Unit 2.

Vocabulary

Important terms in Unit 2:

Numbers All Around Museum A routine that promotes number awareness and is used throughout the year as the class assembles specific collections of numbers.

Math Boxes Math problems inside "math boxes" that provide an opportunity for reviewing ideas and practicing skills.

unit boxes Boxes that contain labels or units of measure used in problems. For example, in problems involving children in the class, the unit box would be as shown on the right.

Unit
children

analog clock Clock with an hour hand and a minute hand.

digital clock Clock with number displays.

Do-Anytime Activities

To work with your child on the concepts taught in this unit and in Unit 1, try these interesting and rewarding activities:

1 Point out common uses of numbers, such as page numbers, the numbers on clocks, phones, cereal boxes, and the numbers in house addresses.

2 Help your child estimate the time using only the hour hand on an analog clock.

3 Help your child practice saying the telephone numbers of relatives and friends.

4 Count various sets of nickels and pennies together.

Have fun with these and all other mathematics activities!

Use with Lesson 1.14.

As You Help Your Child with Homework

As your child brings home assignments, you may want to go over the instructions together, clarifying them as necessary. The answers listed below will guide you through this unit's Home Links.

Home Link 2.6

2. 5 o'clock, 9 o'clock

3.

Home Link 2.7

1. Abraham Lincoln, Lincoln Memorial

2.

5

6

7

8

9

10

Home Link 2.8

2. Thomas Jefferson, Monticello

3. 5, 10

Home Link 2.9

2. 15 pennies

3. 32 tally marks

Home Link 2.10

1. 2 nickels

2. a. Ⓝ Ⓝ Ⓟ, 11 cents

   b. Ⓝ Ⓝ Ⓟ, 11 cents

Home Link 2.11

Game 1: 17¢, 16¢, Sabine

Game 2: 16¢, 20¢, Tony

Game 3: 28¢, 25¢, Sabine

Home Link 2.12

1. 8 o'clock, 11 o'clock

Building Skills through Games

In this unit, your child will practice numeration and money skills by playing the following games:

Rolling for 50

Players roll a die to navigate their way on the number grid. The first player to cross FINISH wins the game!

Top-It

Each player turns over a card. Whoever has the higher number card keeps both cards. The winner has more cards when the whole deck has been turned over.

Penny Cup

Starting with a cup and a specified number of pennies, one player turns the cup upside down, hiding some of the pennies. The other player counts the visible pennies and guesses how many pennies are hidden underneath.

Penny Guessing

Players guess how many nickels they can trade for their partner's pile of pennies.

Penny-Nickel Exchange

Partners put 20 pennies and 10 nickels in a pile. Each player rolls a die and collects the number of pennies shown on the die. Whenever players have at least 5 pennies, they say "Exchange!" and trade their pennies for a nickel.

High Roller

Players roll two dice and keep the die with the greater number (the "high roller"). Players roll the other die again and count on from the "high roller" to get the sum of the two dice.

Use with Lesson 1.14.

Telephone Numbers

Family Note

Work with your child on memorizing important telephone numbers, including any emergency daytime numbers other than your home number. Also, help your child find other examples of uses of numbers. These uses might include some or all of the following:

- Measurements of length, weight, volume, and so on
- Dates and times
- Tables
- Temperatures
- Counts
- Addresses and license plates
- Costs

Please return this Home Link to school tomorrow.

1. Write your area code and home telephone number.

(____ ____ ____) ____ ____ ____ – ____ ____ ____ ____

     (area code)   (telephone number)

2. Write an emergency number with the area code. This number could be for a relative or neighbor. It might be the number for the local police department.

(____ ____ ____) ____ ____ ____ – ____ ____ ____ ____

3. Write your first, second, and third names.

_____

4. Bring more examples of numbers to school.

Counting Up and Back

Family Note

To reinforce various types of counting, listen as your child counts by 1s and 10s. Children love to count for someone, and doing so provides wonderful practice in this essential first grade skill.

Please return this Home Link to school tomorrow.

1. Count for someone at home.
Count up by 1s, starting with 1. I counted to _____.

2. Count back by 1s. Start with 20 or
the highest number you can. I started with _____.

3. Count up by 10s. Start with 10. I counted to _____.

4. Count back by 10s. Start with 50 or
the highest number you can. I started with _____.

5. Explain to someone at home how to use the number grid to help with counts.

									0
1	2	3	4	5	6	7	8	9	10
11	12	13	14	15	16	17	18	19	20
21	22	23	24	25	26	27	28	29	30
31	32	33	34	35	36	37	38	39	40
41	42	43	44	45	46	47	48	49	50
51	52	53	54	55	56	57	58	59	60
61	62	63	64	65	66	67	68	69	70
71	72	73	74	75	76	77	78	79	80
81	82	83	84	85	86	87	88	89	90
91	92	93	94	95	96	97	98	99	100
101	102	103	104	105	106	107	108	109	110

Two-Fisted Penny Addition

Family Note

By playing *Two-Fisted Penny Addition*, you are helping your child build a foundation for learning the basic addition facts. Knowing the basic facts will be useful later on, when your child will be solving more difficult addition and subtraction problems mentally.

Please return this Home Link to school tomorrow.

Play *Two-Fisted Penny Addition* with someone at home:

• Put 10 pennies on the table.

• Grab some pennies with one hand.
  Pick up the rest with the other hand.

• On a piece of paper, draw 2 large circles to show hands.
  Place 1 pile of pennies in each circle.

• Count the pennies on each circle.

• Write how many pennies are on each circle.

• Take turns with your partner.

1. Start with 10 pennies.

Number of Pennies in One Hand	Number of Pennies in the Other Hand

2. Start with 15 pennies.

Number of Pennies in One Hand	Number of Pennies in the Other Hand

Name _____ Date _____

Family Note

When working with "before" and "after" numbers in the table below, start with small numbers—up to 15. Then, if your child is doing well, increase the size of the numbers. Also, ask your child to suggest numbers to write in the middle column of the table.

Please return this Home Link to school tomorrow.

Ask someone to write a number in the middle column.

• Write the number that comes *after* that number.

• Write the number that comes *before* that number.

Try this with many different numbers.

Before	Number	After
Example 8	9	10

Clocks and Watches

Family Note

Both analog clocks (clocks that have hour hands and minute hands) and digital clocks should be included in the tallies in the table below. In today's lesson, we observed what happens to the hour hand on an analog clock as the minute hand moves around the clock face. In the next lesson, we will practice telling the time when the minute hand is pointing to 12.

Please return this Home Link to school tomorrow.

Ask someone to help you find all of the clocks and watches in your home.

Record the numbers with tally marks.

	Tallies
Clocks	
Watches	

Total: _____

Draw a picture of the most interesting clock or watch you found. It might be interesting because of the way it looks or where it is located.

Name _____   Date _____

Family Note

We have just begun our work with telling time. Your child is working on telling time to the hour. Ask your child to show times on the hour on the paper clock, as in Part 1 below.

Please return this Home Link to school tomorrow, but keep your child's paper clock for future use.

1. Show your paper clock to someone at home.

• Show 3 o'clock.

• Show 11 o'clock.

• Ask someone to name an hour for you to show.

2. Record the time.

_____ o'clock   _____ o'clock

3. Draw the hour hand.

7 o'clock   1 o'clock

Ordering Numbers

Family Note

Over the next few weeks, we will be "getting to know coins" in our class. In the next lesson, we will learn about pennies. Here is some background information: Abraham Lincoln appears on the HEADS side. The Lincoln Memorial is shown on the TAILS side.

Your child is also learning how to order and compare numbers. Dominoes are a perfect tool for practicing this skill. If you have dominoes at home, you may want to play ordering games with your child. At first, use consecutive numbers like 1, 2, 3, and 4.

Please return this Home Link to school tomorrow.

1. Get a penny.

- Who is on the HEADS side? _____

- What is on the TAILS side? _____

2. Cut out the dominoes at the bottom of the page.

- Count the total number of dots on each domino.

- Put the dominoes in order from least to greatest number of dots.

- Tape the dominoes in order on the back of this page.

- Write the total number of dots under each domino.

Nickels

Family Note

During the next few weeks, our class will learn about coins. For our next math lesson, your child will need 5 nickels. Please put these nickels in a sealed envelope with your child's name on it so that they will not get lost. (Your child will also need 10 dimes and 2 quarters in the coming days.)

Here is some background information about nickels: Thomas Jefferson appears on the HEADS side of the nickel. Monticello, Jefferson's home in Virginia, appears on the TAILS side.

Please return this Home Link to school tomorrow.

---

1. Ask someone at home for 5 nickels you can bring to school. Use one of them for this Home Link.

---

2. Look closely at a nickel. Ask someone to help you answer the following questions:

- Who is on the HEADS side? _____

- What is on the TAILS side? _____

---

3. Ask someone to trade you the correct number of pennies for your nickel.

- How many pennies did the person give you?

_____ pennies

- How many pennies would you get for 2 nickels?

_____ pennies

- Explain to someone at home how you found your answer.

Name _____   Date _____

Counting by 5s

Family Note

Counting by 5s is a useful skill for counting combinations of coins that include nickels. A good way to practice this skill is to count tally marks.

Please return this Home Link to school tomorrow.

1. Count by 5s for someone at home.

I counted up to _____.

2. Tell someone at home how many pennies you will get for 3 nickels.

3. Count the tally marks below.

̶H̶H̶T ̶H̶H̶T ̶H̶H̶T ̶H̶H̶T ̶H̶H̶T ̶H̶H̶T //

I counted _____ tally marks.

4. Draw some tally marks below.
Count them for someone at home.

I drew _____ tally marks.

Pennies and Nickels

Family Note

First graders do not always know how to represent an amount with the fewest number of coins. That's okay. At this stage, the important thing is that your child understands that 5 pennies can be exchanged for 1 nickel.

In a few days, we are going to set up a "store" in our classroom. Some children will take on the role of shopkeeper, others the role of shopper. Please send some old, inexpensive items (such as rulers, toy cars, stickers, or a ball and jacks) to school for us to use in our store. Thank you!

Please return this Home Link to school tomorrow.

1. Tell or show someone at home how many nickels you get for 10 pennies.

2. For each problem, write how much the coins are worth. Use Ⓟ and Ⓝ to show the amount with fewer coins.

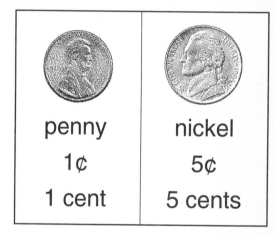

penny	nickel
1¢	5¢
1 cent	5 cents

Example Ⓟ Ⓟ Ⓟ Ⓟ Ⓟ Ⓟ Ⓟ is the same as Ⓝ Ⓟ Ⓟ.

This is 7 cents.

a. Ⓟ Ⓟ Ⓟ Ⓟ Ⓟ Ⓟ Ⓟ Ⓟ Ⓟ Ⓟ Ⓟ is the same as

This is ____ cents.

b. Ⓝ Ⓟ Ⓟ Ⓟ Ⓟ Ⓟ Ⓟ is the same as

This is ____ cents.

Nickel/Penny Grab

Family Note

In class, we have been playing *Nickel/Penny Grab*. Ask your child to tell you how to play. The game provides practice in counting combinations of pennies and nickels and then comparing amounts of money. If your child is having trouble doing this, use real coins to model the problems. Another way to help your child is to trade nickels for pennies and then count the pennies.

 We will be doing a lot of work with money exchanges and with counting money. But do not expect your child to master these skills at this time.

Please return this Home Link to school tomorrow.

Sabine and Tony played *Nickel/Penny Grab.*
They played 3 games. Here is what happened:

Game 1: Sabine grabbed 2 nickels and 7 pennies.

She had _____¢.

Tony grabbed 3 nickels and 1 penny. He had _____¢.

Circle who grabbed more: **Sabine** *or* **Tony**

Game 2: Sabine grabbed 2 nickels and 6 pennies.

She had _____¢.

Tony grabbed 3 nickels and 5 pennies. He had _____¢.

Circle who grabbed more: **Sabine** *or* **Tony**

Game 3: Sabine grabbed 4 nickels and 8 pennies.

She had _____¢.

Tony grabbed 3 nickels and 10 pennies. He had _____¢.

Circle who grabbed more: **Sabine** *or* **Tony**

Telling Time

Family Note

We have not practiced telling time in class for several days, so your child may need some review. Use the paper clock that your child brought home several days ago to practice telling time. If you no longer have the paper clock, you might use a small real clock instead.

Please return this Home Link to school tomorrow.

1. Record the time.

_____ o'clock

_____ o'clock

2. Draw the hour hand.

3:00

6:00

3. On the back of this page, draw a picture of something you will do at home tonight. Have someone help you figure out about what time (to the nearest hour) you will do the activity. Show the time on your paper clock.

Counting Money

Family Note

This Home Link may be challenging for your child. It not only reviews some of the concepts we have covered in this unit, but it also requires your child to apply these concepts to new situations. Do not worry if this page is challenging—we will be working on counting money throughout the year. Encourage your child to use real coins to model the problems.

Please return this Home Link to school tomorrow.

1. Have someone at home help you collect a small container of pennies and nickels. Take a handful of the coins.

2. How many coins are in one handful? How much are they worth?

   _____ pennies = _____¢   _____ nickels = _____¢

3. How much are the pennies and nickels worth together?

   I counted _____¢ in one handful.

4. Circle two items that you would like to buy.

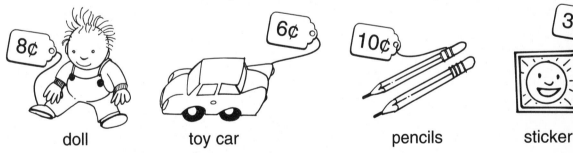

8¢   doll   6¢   toy car   10¢   pencils   3¢   sticker

   a. Which item costs more? _____

   b. How much more does it cost? _____¢ more

Challenge

5. How much do the two items cost together? _____¢

Unit 3: Visual Patterns, Number Patterns, and Counting

Children will have several experiences with patterns that use objects, colors, and numbers.

Count by 10s.	0, 10, 20
Count by 5s.	0, 5, 10, 15, 20
Count by 2s.	0, 2, 4, 6, 8, 10
Count by 3s.	0, 3, 6, 9, 12

2, 4, 6, 8, 10, 12.
12 is an even number.

As patterns with numbers are investigated, children will take a closer look at the common patterns found in odd and even numbers. They will observe the patterns in the ending digits of counts by 2s, 3s, 5s, and 10s. Frames-and-Arrows diagrams will be introduced to help children in their investigation of number sequences. (See explanation on next page.)

Children will also continue to develop their time-telling and money-counting skills. They will practice telling time on the hour and the half-hour. And they will continue to work with real coins, so we would like you to send 10 dimes to school to add to your child's tool-kit coin collection. (As before, please be sure to send these coins in a sealed envelope with your child's name on it.)

Finally, we will begin work on addition and subtraction. This is an important topic—it will be developed throughout the year. It is not too early for children to begin solving some very simple problems.

Vocabulary

Important terms in Unit 3:

number grid A table in which consecutive numbers are usually arranged in rows of ten.

									0
1	2	3	4	5	6	7	8	9	10
11	12	13	14	15	16	17	18	19	20
21	22	23	24	25	26	27	28	29	30
31	32	33	34	35	36	37	38	39	40
41	42	43	44	45	46	47	48	49	50

Number grids are used to develop place-value concepts and addition and subtraction problem-solving strategies.

pattern A predictable arrangement of items.

even number Any whole number that ends in 0, 2, 4, 6, or 8. An even number of objects can always be broken into pairs.

odd number Any whole number that ends in 1, 3, 5, 7, or 9. When an odd number of objects is broken into pairs, there will always be one object that cannot be paired.

Frames and Arrows Diagrams that are used to represent number sequences or sets of numbers that are ordered according to a rule. Each frame contains one of the numbers in the sequence. Each arrow stands for the rule that tells which number goes in the next frame.

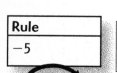

Rule
−5

35 → 30 → 25 → 20 → 15 → 10

The Family Note on Home Link 3.8, which you will receive later, provides a more detailed description of Frames and Arrows.

Use with Lesson 2.14

Do-Anytime Activities

To work with your child on concepts taught in this unit and in previous units, try these interesting and rewarding activities:

1 Count and pair objects found around the house and determine whether there's an odd or even number of items.

2 Using the same collection of objects, arrange them to make an ongoing pattern. Then have your child make and describe his or her own pattern.

3 Using the number grid, select a number and have your child point to the number that is 1 more or 1 less than the selected number. Do problems like this: "Start at 28. Count back (or up) 5 spaces. On which number do you land?"

Counting back from 28

									0
1	2	3	4	5	6	7	8	9	10
11	12	13	14	15	16	17	18	19	20
21	22	23	24	25	26	27	28	29	30
31	32	33	34	35	36	37	38	39	40
41	42	43	44	45	46	47	48	49	50

Use with Lesson 2.14.

As You Help Your Child with Homework

As your child brings home assignments, you may want to go over the instructions together, clarifying them as necessary. The answers listed below will guide you through this unit's Home Links.

Home Link 3.3

1. 6   **2.** 7   **3.** 10   **4.** 15   **5.** 11   **6.** 7

Home Link 3.6

1. 7   **2.** 7   **3.** 5   **4.** 16
5. 10   **6.** 1   **7.** 12   **8.** 2

Home Link 3.7

1. 5 o'clock, 7 o'clock

2. half-past 2 o'clock, half-past 9 o'clock

Home Link 3.8

Home Link 3.9

Home Link 3.10

1. Franklin Roosevelt

2. A torch, a laurel, and an oak

3. 5 Ⓟ = 1 Ⓝ; 2 Ⓝ = 1 Ⓓ; 10 Ⓟ = 1 Ⓓ

4. 13¢; 19¢; 30¢

Home Link 3.11

3. Ⓓ; This is 10 cents.

4. Ⓓ Ⓟ Ⓟ; This is 12 cents.

5. Ⓓ Ⓟ Ⓟ Ⓟ Ⓟ; This is 14 cents.

6. Ⓓ Ⓓ Ⓝ; This is 25 cents.

7. Ⓓ Ⓓ; This is 20 cents.

Home Link 3.12

1. 25¢, or $0.25   **2.** 45¢, or $0.45   **3.** 23¢, or $0.23
4. 37¢, or $0.37   **5.** 43¢, or $0.43

Home Link 3.13

2a. blue   **2b.** yellow

Use with Lesson 2.14

Patterns

Family Note

Patterns are so important in mathematics that mathematics is sometimes called the "Science of Patterns." Help your child identify patterns in and around your home and in the outside world.

Some suggestions for places to look for patterns:

- floor tiles
- carpeting
- window panes
- curtains
- wallpaper
- fences

Please return this Home Link to school tomorrow.

1. Find at least two patterns in your home. Draw the patterns you find.

2. If you have articles of clothing (such as a shirt or a pair of socks) that have patterns on them, please wear those clothes to school tomorrow!

Odd and Even Numbers

Family Note

As children learn about the concept of odd and even numbers, extend this activity to include the number of people at home or the numbers of various objects, such as chairs, windows, videos, and books on a shelf.

Please return this Home Link to school tomorrow.

1. Count the number of people in your home.

There are _____ people in my home.

Is this number **even** or **odd**? _____

2. Tell someone at home about odd and even numbers.

Write some **odd** numbers here: _____, _____, _____, _____

Write some **even** numbers here: _____, _____, _____, _____

3. Count the number of a type of object in your home. Write the number and the type of object.

There are _____ _____ in my home.

Is this number **even** or **odd**? _____

Number-Line Hops

Family Note

We are beginning to use the number line as a tool for solving addition and subtraction problems. Help your child answer the questions below by moving a finger from number to number on the number line. Make sure that your child is counting the number of hops and not the numbers themselves.

Please return this Home Link to school tomorrow.

Use the number line on the side of this page to help you answer the questions.

Example

Start at 5. Count the hops to 11. How many hops? __6__

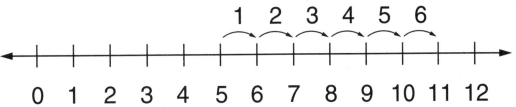

1. How many hops from 4 to 10? _____

2. How many hops from 8 to 15? _____

3. How many hops from 9 to 19? _____

4. How many hops from 1 to 16? _____

Challenge

5. Start at 3. Go 11 hops. Where do you end up? _____

6. If you go 7 hops and land on 14, where did you start? _____

Use with Lesson 3.3.

0
1
2
3
4
5
6
7
8
9
10
11
12
13
14
15
16
17
18
19
20
21
22
23
24
25

55

More Odd and Even Numbers

Family Note

In class we are learning to identify even and odd numbers by looking at the last digit in a number. All even numbers end in 0, 2, 4, 6, or 8. All odd numbers end in 1, 3, 5, 7, or 9. Ask your child to explain how to tell whether a number is even or odd. Give examples of odd and even numbers for your child to identify.

Please return this Home Link to school tomorrow.

1. Write the number part of your address below.

_____

Is this number **odd** or **even**? _____

Tell someone you know.

2. Are the addresses across the street odd or even?

_____

3. Write an even number less than 50. Show it with tally marks.

_____

4. Write an odd number less than 50. Show it with tally marks

_____

Challenge

5. Write the biggest even number you know. _____

Ask or tell someone how to read this number.

Number Lines and Counting

Family Note

Listen as your child tells you about number lines and counts. Be sure he or she records the numbers counted. Provide several objects, such as pennies or dried beans, for your child to use to count by 10s, 5s, 2s, and 3s.

Please return this Home Link to school tomorrow.

Tell someone at home what you know about number lines and counting patterns.

Count by 10s, 5s, 2s, and 3s. Begin at 0 each time.

Then go back and circle all the odd numbers on the number line.

Count by 10s. 0, _____, _____

Count by 5s. 0, _____, _____, _____, _____

Count by 2s. 0, _____, _____, _____, _____

Count by 3s. 0, _____, _____, _____, _____

0
1
2
3
4
5
6
7
8
9
10
11
12
13
14
15
16
17
18
19
20

More Number-Line Hops

Family Note

We are beginning to work with number models like $3 + 2 = 5$ and $8 - 5 = 3$. We are solving them by counting up and back on the number line. Ask your child to show you how to do this. If your child has trouble with the Challenge problems, make up number stories that use these numbers. For example, for $7 + 3 = $ ___, you might make up the following story: "You have 7 pennies. I give you 3 more. How many pennies do you have now?" Your child can use real pennies to find the answer.

Please return this Home Link to school tomorrow.

Use the number line to help you solve these problems.

1. Start at 4. Count up 3 hops. Where do you

end up? _____ $4 + 3 = $ _____

2. Start at 12. Count back 5 hops. Where do you

end up? _____ $12 - 5 = $ _____

3. Start at 11. Count back 6 hops. Where do you

end up? _____ $11 - 6 = $ _____

4. Start at 14. Count up 2 hops. Where do you

end up? _____ $14 + 2 = $ _____

Challenge

5. $7 + 3 = $ _____   **6.** $6 - 5 = $ _____

7. $2 + 10 = $ _____   **8.** $9 - 7 = $ _____

0
1
2
3
4
5
6
7
8
9
10
11
12
13
14
15
16
17
18
19
20
21
22
23
24
25

Telling Time to the Half-Hour

Family Note

We have just begun working on telling time to the nearest half-hour. Help your child complete these pages. Tell your child at which times, on the hour or half-hour, he or she wakes up and goes to bed on school days. We will continue to practice telling time at school. Have your child tell the time at home when it is close to the hour or half-hour.

Please return these Home Link pages to school tomorrow.

1. Record the time.

_____ o'clock

half-past _____ o'clock

half-past _____ o'clock

half-past _____ o'clock

Telling Time (cont.)

Challenge

2. Draw the hour hand and the minute hand to show the time.

This is the time I wake up in the morning on a school day.

This is the time I go to bed at night before a school day.

Use with Lesson 3.7.

Frames-and-Arrows Diagrams

Family Note

Your child is bringing home an activity you may not be familiar with. It is called "Frames and Arrows."

Frames-and-Arrows diagrams are used with sequences of numbers that follow one after the other according to a special rule. Frames-and-Arrows diagrams are made up of shapes, called **frames,** that are connected by **arrows.** Each frame contains one of the numbers in the sequence. Each arrow stands for the rule that tells how to find which number goes in the next frame. Here is an example of a Frames-and-Arrows diagram:

Rule
Add 2

2 → 4 → 6 → 8 → 10

• The arrow rule is "Add 2" or "Count by 2s."

• In a Frames-and-Arrows problem, some of the information is left out. To solve the problem, you have to find the missing information.

Following are two examples of Frames-and-Arrows problems.

Example 1: Fill in the empty frames according to the arrow rule.

Rule
Subtract 4

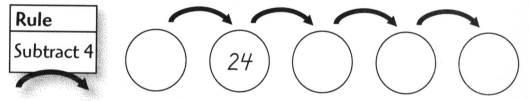

• **Solution:** Write 28 in the first empty frame and 20, 16, and 12 in the frames that follow.

Example 2: Write the arrow rule in the empty box.

Rule

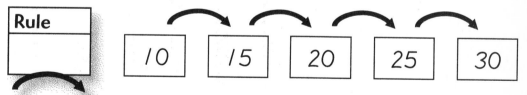

• **Solution:** The arrow rule is "Add 5" or "Count by 5s."

Today in mathematics class, your child has been solving problems like the one in the first example above—problems in which the arrow rule is given and some of the numbers in the frames are missing. In the next lesson, we will start doing problems like the one in the second example above—problems in which the numbers in the frames are given and the arrow rule is missing.

Frames and Arrows (cont.)

**Home Link
3.8**

**Family
Note**

Ask your child to tell you about Frames and Arrows. Then you can play Frames and Arrows with him or her. One player makes up a Frames-and-Arrows problem; the other player solves it.

Please return the second page of this Home Link to school tomorrow. Please save the first page for future reference.

SPECIAL NOTE: We are continuing to practice counting money in class, using real money. Please send 10 dimes to school for your child's tool-kit coin collection. We will start using the dimes in 2 or 3 days. As usual, please send the coins in a securely fastened envelope with your child's name printed on the outside. Thank you!

Find the missing numbers. How does the rule help you?

Find the Rule

Family Note

Today in mathematics class, we worked with Frames-and-Arrows diagrams in which the rule was missing. You may want to refer back to the Home Link 3.8 Family Note and review the Frames-and-Arrows routine.

Please return this Home Link to school tomorrow.

Show someone at home how to find the rules. Then find each rule.

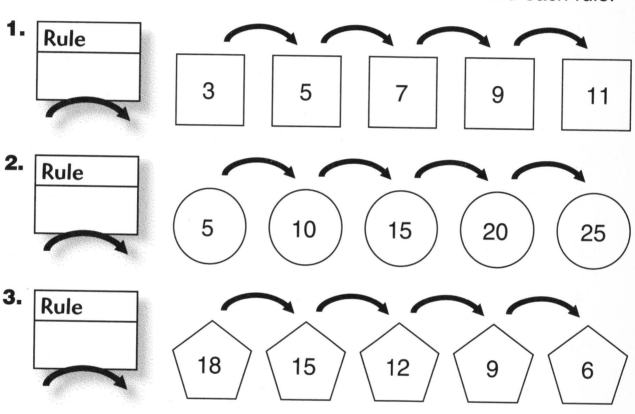

1. Rule _____

3 → 5 → 7 → 9 → 11

2. Rule _____

5 → 10 → 15 → 20 → 25

3. Rule _____

18 → 15 → 12 → 9 → 6

Challenge

4. Find the rule. Then fill in the missing numbers.

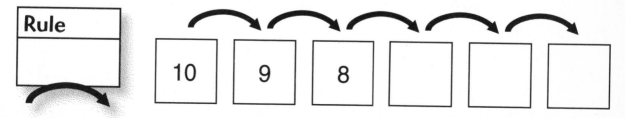

Rule _____

10 → 9 → 8 → ___ → ___ → ___

Family Note

Note that Ⓟ means "penny," Ⓝ means "nickel," and Ⓓ means "dime."
The picture on the HEADS side of a dime is of Franklin Roosevelt. On the TAILS side, there is a torch, a laurel, and an oak.

IMPORTANT: Please send 10 dimes with your child to class tomorrow.

Please return this Home Link to school tomorrow.

Look closely at a dime.

1. Who is on the HEADS side?

_____

2. What is on the TAILS side?

_____

3. How many?

_____ Ⓟ = 1 Ⓝ

_____ Ⓝ = 1 Ⓓ

_____ Ⓟ = 1 Ⓓ

4. How much?

Ⓝ Ⓝ Ⓟ Ⓟ Ⓟ = _____ ¢

Ⓟ Ⓝ Ⓝ Ⓝ Ⓟ Ⓟ Ⓟ = _____ ¢

Ⓝ Ⓝ Ⓝ Ⓝ Ⓝ Ⓝ = _____ ¢

Coin Exchanges

Family Note

First graders do not always know how to represent a given amount of money with the fewest number of coins. That's OK. At this stage, what's important is that your child understands that 5 pennies can be exchanged for 1 nickel and that 10 pennies can be exchanged for 2 nickels or 1 dime.

Please return this Home Link to school tomorrow.

1 cent 1¢	5 cents 5¢	10 cents 10¢
Ⓟ	Ⓝ	Ⓓ

1. Tell or show someone at home how many dimes you get for 4 nickels.

2. Show each amount below using the fewest coins. Use Ⓟ, Ⓝ, and Ⓓ.

(*Hint:* Exchange pennies for nickels and nickels for dimes.) Then write how much the coins are worth.

Example Ⓟ Ⓟ Ⓟ Ⓟ Ⓟ Ⓟ is the same as Ⓝ Ⓟ.

This is 6 cents.

3. Ⓟ Ⓟ Ⓟ Ⓟ Ⓟ Ⓟ Ⓟ Ⓟ Ⓟ Ⓟ is the same as _____.

This is _____ cents.

Coin Exchanges (cont.)

4. Ⓟ Ⓟ Ⓟ Ⓟ Ⓟ Ⓟ Ⓟ Ⓟ Ⓟ Ⓟ Ⓟ is the same

as _____.

This is _____ cents.

5. Ⓝ Ⓟ Ⓟ Ⓟ Ⓟ Ⓟ Ⓟ Ⓟ Ⓟ is the same

as _____.

This is _____ cents.

Challenge

6. Ⓝ Ⓝ Ⓝ Ⓟ Ⓟ Ⓟ Ⓟ Ⓟ Ⓟ Ⓟ Ⓟ Ⓟ is the

same as _____.

This is _____ cents.

7. Ⓝ Ⓟ Ⓝ Ⓟ Ⓝ Ⓟ Ⓟ Ⓟ is the same as _____.

This is _____ cents.

Use with Lesson 3.11.

Counting Coins

1 cent 1¢ $0.01 Ⓟ	5 cents 5¢ $0.05 Ⓝ	10 cents 10¢ $0.10 Ⓓ

How much money? Write each answer in cents and in dollars-and-cents.

1. Ⓓ Ⓝ Ⓝ Ⓝ _____¢ or $_____

2. Ⓓ Ⓓ Ⓝ Ⓝ Ⓝ Ⓝ Ⓝ _____¢ or $_____

3. Ⓓ Ⓝ Ⓝ Ⓟ Ⓟ Ⓟ _____¢ or $_____

4. Ⓓ Ⓓ Ⓝ Ⓝ Ⓝ Ⓟ Ⓟ _____¢ or $_____

Challenge

5. Ⓟ Ⓟ Ⓝ Ⓟ Ⓓ Ⓝ Ⓝ Ⓓ Ⓝ _____¢ or $_____

Family Note

Today we made a line plot for our class like the one below. At this time, your child should begin to see that the tallest column shows the color chosen by the greatest number of people and the shortest column shows the color chosen by the fewest number of people.

Please return this Home Link to school tomorrow.

1. Tell someone at home what the favorite color was in your class today.

2. In Jerry's class, children made this line plot for their favorite color.

   a. What was their **favorite** color?

   _____

   b. What was their **least favorite** color?

   _____

3. Explain to someone at home how you know the answers to these questions.

			B
			B
			B
R	G		B
R	G		B
R	G		B
R	G	Y	B
R	G	Y	B
R	G	Y	B
red	**green**	**yellow**	**blue**

Domino Top-It

**Home Link
3.14**

**Family
Note**

Today your child examined dot patterns on dominoes and learned a game played with dominos. The relationship between the numbers represented by the dots on each domino part and those on the entire domino is useful for work with basic facts.

Domino Top-It is a great game for helping your child practice basic addition facts.

Show someone at home how to play *Domino Top-It.* Use a set of real dominoes, if you have one. Or use the dominoes on the sheets your teacher gave you.

Directions

1. If you have real dominoes, turn them facedown on the table.

If you are using paper dominoes, put them facedown in a stack.

2. Each player turns over a domino.

If you are using paper dominoes, take one from the top of the stack.

3. The player with the larger total number of dots takes both dominoes.

In case of a tie, each player turns over another domino. The player with the larger total takes all the dominoes that are faceup.

4. The game is over when all the dominoes have been played.

The player who has more dominoes wins the game.

Unit 4: Measurement and Basic Facts

Unit 4 focuses primarily on length measurement. Lesson activities will provide various opportunities for children to measure with nonstandard units, such as hand spans and paces, as well as with standard units, such as feet and inches, using a ruler and a tape measure.

Children will practice basic measuring skills, such as marking off units "end to end," aligning the 0-mark of a ruler with one edge of the object being measured, and measuring objects longer than the ruler.

Since most measurements are estimates, you will notice that the language of estimation is used when reporting measurements. For example, measurements are given as *about* 5 hand spans, *a little less than* 8 inches, *almost* 3 feet, and so on.

Children will also practice other measurement skills in this unit. Children will begin to read thermometers that have marks at two-degree intervals, and they will start telling time to the nearest quarter-hour. Children will also explore timelines to begin to develop a sense for the sequence of events with the passage of time.

In this unit, children will begin making number scrolls by writing numbers in extended number grids. This activity not only provides practice with writing numbers, but also helps children develop a sense of the patterns in our place-value system.

−9	−8	−7	−6	−5	−4	−3	−2	−1	0
1	2	3	4	5	6	7	8	9	10
11	12	13	14	15	16	17	18	19	20
21	22	23	24	25	26	27	28	29	30
31	32	33	34	35	36	37	38	39	40
41	42	43	44	45	46	47	48	49	50
51	52	53	54	55	56	57	58	59	60
61	62	63	64	65	66	67	68	69	70
71	72	73	74	75	76	77	78	79	80
81	82	83	84	85	86	87	88	89	90
91	92	93	94	95	96	97	98	99	100

Beginning Scroll Page

In the last two lessons of the unit, children will begin working toward developing addition "fact power." Knowing the basic facts is as important to mathematics as knowing words by sight is to reading. This beginning work uses dominoes as models for the basic addition facts.

$1 + 6 = 7$ $2 + 3 = 5$ $5 + 4 = 9$

Use with Lesson 3.15.

Vocabulary

Important terms in Unit 4:

inch and foot Units of length in the U.S. customary system.

standard unit A uniform unit of measure, such as inch and foot.

timeline A device for showing in sequence when events took place.

number scroll A roll of paper with numbers written on it.

fact power Development of basic number–fact reflexes so that the facts are known without having to figure them out.

$3 + 6 = 9$

$6 + 3 = 9$

$9 - 3 = 6$

$9 - 6 = 3$

addition facts The 100 possible combinations of two one-digit numbers—from the combination with the smallest sum, $0 + 0$, to the combination with the largest sum, $9 + 9$.

+ −	0	1	2	3	4	5	6	7	8	9
0	0	1	2	3	4	5	6	7	8	9
1	1	2	3	4	5	6	7	8	9	10
2	2	3	4	5	6	7	8	9	10	11
3	3	4	5	6	7	8	9	10	11	12
4	4	5	6	7	8	9	10	11	12	13
5	5	6	7	8	9	10	11	12	13	14
6	6	7	8	9	10	11	12	13	14	15
7	7	8	9	10	11	12	13	14	15	16
8	8	9	10	11	12	13	14	15	16	17
9	9	10	11	12	13	14	15	16	17	18

As You Help Your Child with Homework

As your child brings home assignments, you may want to go over the instructions together, clarifying them as necessary. The answers listed below will guide you through this unit's Home Links.

Home Link 4.1

1. 20, 22, 24, 26, 28, 30, 32, 34, 36

2. 50, 52, 54, 56, 58, 60, 62, 64, 66

3. 70°F **4.** 60°F **5.** 80°F **6.** 58°F

7. **8.** **9.** **10.**

Home Link 4.7

1. 10 **2.** 12 **3.** 11

4. 9 **5.** 9 **6.** 9

Home Link 4.8

1. 1 o'clock **2.** half-past 4 o'clock

3. half-past 8 o'clock **4.** 7 o'clock

5. quarter-past 6 o'clock **6.** quarter-to 2 o'clock

Home Link 4.11

1. 6 **2.** 7 **3.** 7 **4.** 9

5. 5 **6.** 5 **7.** 6 **8.** 9

9. 7 **10.** 8 **11.** 7 **12.** 10

Use with Lesson 3.15.

Do-Anytime Activities

To work with your child on the concepts taught in this unit and in previous units, try these interesting and rewarding activities:

1 Use a standard measuring tool (such as a ruler, a tape measure, or a yardstick) to measure objects located in the house. Keep an ongoing list of items measured and their approximate lengths and widths using inches.

2 Practice counting by 2s using a thermometer.

3 Tell the time (on the hour, the half-hour, or the quarter-hour) and have your child draw a picture of a clock representing that time.

4 Have your child tell you the time as minutes after the hour. *For example:* "It is about six-fifteen" or "It is about fifteen minutes after six."

5 Have your child tell you a number story that goes with a given number sentence, such as $3 + 5 = 8$. *For example:* "I had 3 dogs. Then I got 5 more dogs. Now I have 8 dogs!"

Reading Thermometers

Children are beginning to read thermometers marked in two-degree intervals. A skill that you can easily practice with your child at home, which will help with reading temperatures, is to count by 2s. Begin with multiples of 10 (numbers like 10, 20, 30, and so on). For example, start at 50 and count by 2s: 50, 52, 54, 56, 58, 60, and so on.

Please return this Home Link to school tomorrow.

Fill in the frames.

1.

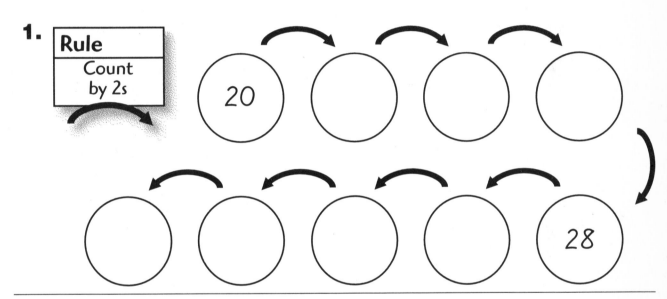

Rule
Count
by 2s

20 ___ ___ ___

___ ___ ___ ___ 28

2.

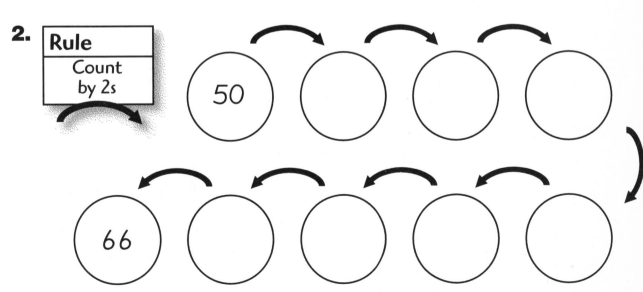

Rule
Count
by 2s

50 ___ ___ ___

66 ___ ___ ___ ___

Write the temperature shown by each thermometer.
Write °F with the temperature.

Challenge

3.

_____

4.

_____

5.

_____

6.

_____

Color the mercury to show each temperature.

Challenge

7.

70° F

8.

50° F

9.

54° F

10.

76° F

Measuring with Hand Spans

Family Note

In today's lesson, we measured objects using nonstandard units like digits (finger widths), hands, fathoms, and hand spans.

One of our discoveries is that we get different measurements for the same obj if different people do the measuring using these units. We will continue this investigation, eventually realizing that standard units, such as feet and inches, provide us with more reliable measurements. Help your child measure his or her bed using hand spans. The drawing below shows a hand span.

Please return this Home Link to school tomorrow.

Measure your bed with your hand span.

1. How many hand spans across is it?

About _____ hand spans

2. How many hand spans long is it?

About _____ hand spans

3. Draw a picture of your bed.

The Foot-Long Foot

Family Note

To help us investigate the measuring unit "feet," please help your child trace each family member's foot using different-color crayons.

Please return this Home Link to school tomorrow.

Compare the foot-long foot to the feet of members of your family.

Here is what you do:

1. Trace each person's foot onto the foot-long foot. Use a different-color crayon for each person's foot.

2. Label each traced foot with the person's name.

3. Talk about why it is not a good idea for people to use their own feet for measuring things.

Measuring with Inches

Family Note

We are just beginning to measure to the nearest inch. Do not expect your child to be proficient with this skill at this time. We will be practicing throughout the year. To help your child, make sure that he or she lines up one end of the object being measured with the "0-mark" on the ruler. Help your child find the closest inch mark at the other end of the object. (We have used the $\frac{1}{2}$ inch marks to find the closest inch marks).

Please return this Home Link to school tomorrow.

Cut out the ruler at the bottom of this page. Use it to measure four small objects. Draw a picture of each object. Write the measurements.

1.

About _____ inches long

2.

About _____ inches long

3.

About _____ inches long

4.

About _____ inches long

```
0   INCHES   1       2       3       4       5       6
```

Measuring with a Ruler

Family Note

This activity is the same as the activity on the previous Home Link, except that this ruler is marked in sixteenths of an inch. Although the marks for fractions of an inch may distract your child, this ruler is the same as the tool-kit ruler we use at school. Your child may find that it helps to "color" the inch marks.

Have your child measure objects to the nearest inch. Make sure your child lines up one end of the object being measured with the "0-mark" on the ruler.

Please return this Home Link to school tomorrow.

Cut out the ruler at the bottom of this page. Use it to measure four small objects to the nearest inch. Draw a picture of each object. Record your measurements.

1.

About _____ inches long

2.

About _____ inches long

3.

About _____ inches long

4.

_____

About _____ inches long

0 INCHES   1   2   3   4   5   6

Name _____   Date _____

Family Note

In class, we have been working with linear measures, using rulers and tape measures. The length of an object is an example of a linear measure.

Help your child find rulers and tape measures in your home. You and your child may also include other kinds of measuring tools, such as scales that measure weight, measuring cups that measure capacity, and so on.

Please return this Home Link to school tomorrow.

Name and draw 3 measuring tools in your home.

Example

1.

2.

3.

Name _____ Date _____

Family Note

Dominoes are a great way to develop readiness for addition and subtraction facts. We will do a lot of work with dominoes this year.

Please return this Home Link to school tomorrow.

Draw the missing dots on each domino.
Write the total number of dots.

1. _____

8   2

2. _____

6   6

3. _____

5   6

4. _____

4   5

5. _____

7   2

6. _____

3   6

Challenge

Draw missing dots on each domino.
Write the numbers for each set of dots and for the total.

Make up your own.

7. _____

_____

8. _____

9. _____

Telling Time

Family Note

Before today, we have been learning to tell time on the hour and the half-hour. Today we began to learn how to tell time on the quarter-hour.

Please return this Home Link to school tomorrow.

Record the time.

1.

_____ o'clock

2.

half-past

_____ o'clock

3.

half-past

_____ o'clock

Challenge

4.

_____ o'clock

5.

quarter-past

_____ o'clock

6.

quarter-to

_____ o'clock

My Timeline

Family Note

Talk about important events that have happened in your family since your child was born. Identify one main event for each year and help your child decide what to draw to represent that event. Use events like the birth of a brother or sister, moving to a new home, and so on.

If you prefer, you can help your child select representative pictures from magazines and tape or glue them in order on this page.

Please return this Home Link to school tomorrow or the day after tomorrow.

Write the years below. Then on the back of this page, draw pictures of important things that happened in your family each year since you were born.

My 8th birthday

My 7th birthday

My 6th birthday

My 5th birthday

My 4th birthday

My 3rd birthday

My 2nd birthday

My 1st birthday

I was born.

Number Grids

Family Note

Ordering numbers in a grid is important in identifying number patterns and developing number power. You and your child may want to talk about any patterns in the section of a number grid shown below.

Please return this Home Link to school tomorrow.

1. Tell your family how you filled in number grids and made scrolls.

2. Ask if your family knows about any other kinds of scrolls.

3. Show someone how you can fill in the bottom 3 rows of this number grid.

									100
101									
				115					
									130

Review

How much money? Write each answer in cents and dollars-and-cents.

4. Ⓓ Ⓝ Ⓝ Ⓟ Ⓟ Ⓟ _____¢ or $_____

5. Ⓓ Ⓓ Ⓓ Ⓝ Ⓝ Ⓟ _____¢ or $_____

Family Note

We have started our work with basic addition facts. The basic facts include sums for the facts from 0 + 0 through 9 + 9. At this beginning stage, your child may still need to count the total number of dots on the dominoes to complete the problems.

Please return this Home Link to school tomorrow.

Find the sums.

1.
```
    4
  + 2
  ‾‾‾
    6
```

2.
```
    6
  + 1
  ‾‾‾
    7
```

3.
```
    7
  + 0
  ‾‾‾
    7
```

4.
```
    8
  + 1
  ‾‾‾
    9
```

5.   1 + 4 = 5

6.   5 = 2 + 3

7.   3 + 3 = 6

8.   9 = 0 + 9

9.
```
    3
  + 4
  ‾‾‾
    7
```

10.
```
    2
  + 6
  ‾‾‾
    8
```

11.
```
    5
  + 2
  ‾‾‾
    7
```

12.
```
    8
  + 2
  ‾‾‾
   10
```

Challenge

13. Draw a domino of your choice.
Write a fact to go with it.

_____

Name _____   Date _____

Color-by-Number

Family Note

We are continuing our work with addition facts. Now we are working with facts using +0, +1, +2 (such as 3 + 0, 5 + 1, and 8 + 2) and doubles facts (such as 2 + 2 and 4 + 4).

Please return this Home Link to school tomorrow.

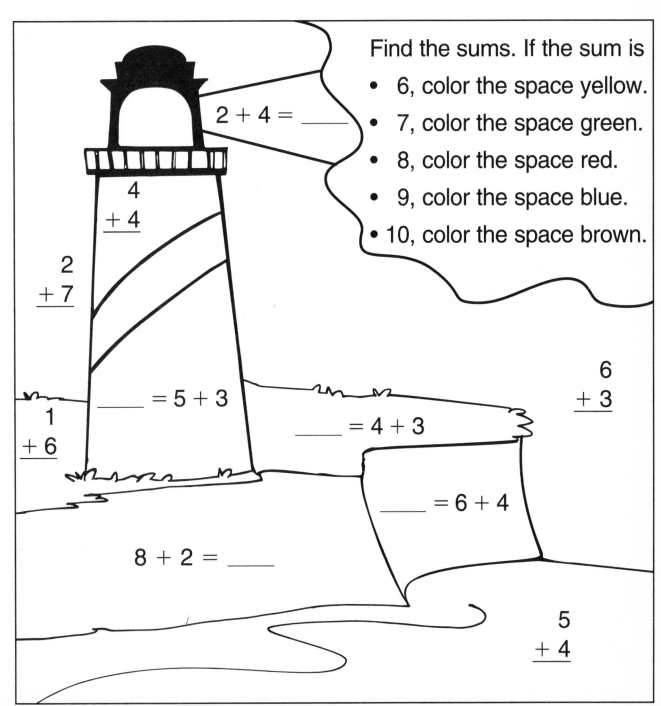

Find the sums. If the sum is

- 6, color the space yellow.
- 7, color the space green.
- 8, color the space red.
- 9, color the space blue.
- 10, color the space brown.

$2 + 4 =$ ____

$\begin{array}{r} 4 \\ + 4 \\ \hline \end{array}$

$\begin{array}{r} 2 \\ + 7 \\ \hline \end{array}$

$\begin{array}{r} 1 \\ + 6 \\ \hline \end{array}$

____ $= 5 + 3$

____ $= 4 + 3$

____ $= 6 + 4$

$\begin{array}{r} 6 \\ + 3 \\ \hline \end{array}$

$8 + 2 =$ ____

$\begin{array}{r} 5 \\ + 4 \\ \hline \end{array}$

Use with Lesson 4.12.

107

Unit 5: Place Value, Number Stories, and Basic Facts

As their work in mathematics progresses, children are beginning to use larger numbers. In Unit 5, children will begin to explore the system we use for writing large numbers by focusing on the idea of **place value.** For example, in the number 72, 7 is in the tens place, so there are "7 tens," and 2 is in the ones place, so there are "2 ones." Children will use base-10 blocks to represent numbers and to find the sums of two numbers. They will also use place value to determine "greater than" and "less than" relationships.

Later in this unit, children will continue to work with addition facts. Shortcuts for learning facts will be introduced. One shortcut is the **turn-around rule,** which states that the order in which numbers are added does not change the sum. For example, 4 + 3 and 3 + 4 both equal 7. Your child will also learn the meaning of adding 0 and 1 to any number. Knowing these shortcuts will make the task of learning addition facts easier.

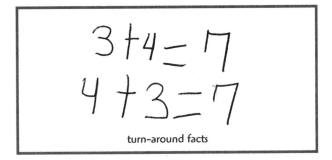

turn-around facts

Children will also practice place value and addition and subtraction facts by acting out number stories. They will act out these stories using concrete objects and begin to represent the stories with **number models.** (See this unit's vocabulary list for more information on number models.)

Children have explored many number patterns in previous lessons. **"What's My Rule?"** is a routine introduced in this unit and found throughout *Everyday Mathematics* that provides practice with number patterns and number relationships. You will receive more detailed information about this routine when we begin to use it in class.

Please keep this Family Letter for reference as your child works through Unit 5.

Vocabulary

Important terms in Unit 5:

cube A base-10 block that represents 1.

long A base-10 block that represents 10.

flat A base-10 block that represents 100.

place value The quantity a digit represents in a number. This quantity, or value, is determined by the digit's position in the number. For example, in the number 52, the 5 represents 5 tens, and the 2 represents 2 ones.

number model A numerical representation that shows how the parts of a number story are related.

Example of a number story:

Seven lions are lying in the sun. Three more lions join them. How many lions are there altogether?

Example of a number model:

$$7 + 3 = 10$$

Unit
lions

turn-around addition facts Two addition facts in which the same two numbers are being added, but they appear in a different order. For example, 5 + 4 = 9 and 4 + 5 = 9 are turn-around addition facts.

doubles fact An addition fact in which both numbers being added are the same. For example, 5 + 5 = 10; 2 + 2 = 4; and 6 + 6 = 12 are all double facts.

function machine A diagram of an imaginary machine programmed to process numbers according to a certain rule. A number (input) is put into the machine and is transformed into a second number (output) through the application of a rule.

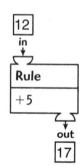

"What's My Rule?" A routine that consists of a set of number pairs in which the numbers in each pair are related to each other according to the same rule. The problems are usually displayed in table format, in which two of the three parts are known. The goal is to find the unknown part.

Rule
+5

in	out
2	7
5	10
7	12
6	11

Use with Lesson 4.13.

Do-Anytime Activities

To work with your child on the concepts taught in this unit and in previous units, try these interesting and rewarding activities:

1 Tell addition and subtraction number stories. Have your child solve the problems using various household objects and then record the answers in number models. Remember to give a context for the numbers, such as coins, animals, types of clothing, and so on.

2 Encourage your child to make up some number stories, too.

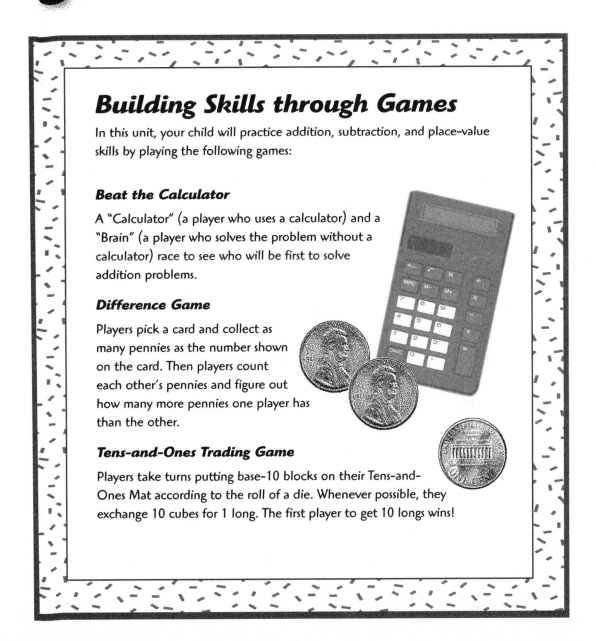

Building Skills through Games

In this unit, your child will practice addition, subtraction, and place-value skills by playing the following games:

Beat the Calculator

A "Calculator" (a player who uses a calculator) and a "Brain" (a player who solves the problem without a calculator) race to see who will be first to solve addition problems.

Difference Game

Players pick a card and collect as many pennies as the number shown on the card. Then players count each other's pennies and figure out how many more pennies one player has than the other.

Tens-and-Ones Trading Game

Players take turns putting base-10 blocks on their Tens-and-Ones Mat according to the roll of a die. Whenever possible, they exchange 10 cubes for 1 long. The first player to get 10 longs wins!

As You Help Your Child with Homework

As your child brings home assignments, you may want to go over the instructions together, clarifying them as necessary. The answers listed below will guide you through this unit's Home Links.

Home Link 5.1

1. 56   **2.** 73   **3.** 12   **4.** 49

Home Link 5.2

1. 20, 30, 40, 50, 60, 70

2. 120, 110, 100, 90, 80, 70

3. 88, 78, 68, 58, 48, 38

4. 4, 14, 24, 34, 44, 54

Home Link 5.3

1. >   **2.** <   **3.** =   **4.** <

5. >   **6.** <   **7.** >   **8.** =

Home Link 5.4

1. 32¢, or $0.32   **2.** 36¢, or $0.36

3. 38¢, or $0.38   **4.** 50¢, or $0.50

Home Link 5.5

1. 8   **2.** 12   **3.** 4

4. 6   **5.** 3   **6.** 6

7. 6   **8.** 9   **9.** 4

10.

$$\begin{array}{r} 8 \\ +\,8 \\ \hline 16 \end{array}$$

11.

$5 + \underline{\quad 5 \quad} = 10$

Home Link 5.6

1. <   **2.** >   **3.** =

4. <   **5.** <   **6.** <

Home Link 5.7

1. Bart; 4¢   **2.** Martha; 7¢

3. Maria; 8¢   **4.** Michelle; 11¢

Home Link 5.9

1. >   **2.** <   **3.** =

4. =   **5.** =

Home Link 5.10

1. 6 + 3 = 9   **2.** 3 + 6 = 9

3. 5 + 4 = 9   **4.** 4 + 5 = 9

Home Link 5.12

1. Rule +1

in	out
6	7
14	15
26	27
19	20
9	10

Your turn: ____

2. Rule −2

in	out
10	8
22	20
25	23
12	10
21	19

Your turn: ____

3. Rule +10

in	out
36	46
19	29
62	72
25	35

Your turn: ____

4. Rule half of

in	out
2	1
4	2
6	3
8	4

Your turn: ____

Home Link 5.13

1. Rule +3

2. Rule −10

in	out
13	3
26	16
45	35

4. Rule +2

in	out
3	5
1	3
0	2

Use with Lesson 4.13.

Tens-and-Ones Riddles

Family Note

We have begun to work on place value using base-10 blocks. The blocks shown in the tens columns are called *longs* and the blocks shown in the ones columns are called *cubes*. It takes 10 cubes to make 1 long. On this page, your child is writing the numbers shown with longs and cubes. The Challenge problem is difficult because you need to exchange 10 of the cubes for 1 long before you can write the number. If your child has trouble with this problem, you might use dimes for the longs and pennies for the cubes and exchange 10 pennies for a dime.

Please return this Home Link to school tomorrow.

Example

Tens	Ones

What number am I? __28__

1.

Tens	Ones

What number am I? _____

2.

Tens	Ones

What number am I? _____

3.

Tens	Ones

What number am I? _____

Challenge

4.

Tens	Ones

What number am I? _____

Frames-and-Arrows Diagrams

Find the missing numbers in these diagrams.

1.

Rule
+10

20 ◯ ◯ ◯ 60 ◯

2.

Rule
−10

120 ◯ ◯ ◯ 80 ◯

3.

Rule
Count back by 10s

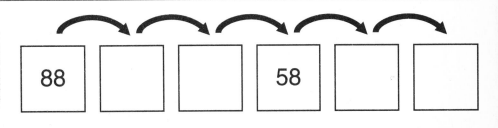

88 ☐ ☐ 58 ☐ ☐

Challenge

4.

Rule
Add 10

◯ 14 ◯ ◯ 44 ◯

Relation Symbols

Family Note

The relation symbols < and > were introduced in this lesson. The symbol < means *is less than* and the symbol > means *is greater than*. These symbols will be used from now on in the same way we use the symbol = for *is equal to* or *equals*. For example, instead of writing 5 *is less than* 8, we will write 5 < 8.

It takes time for children to learn the correct use of these symbols. One way to help your child identify the correct symbol is to draw two dots near the larger number and one dot near the smaller number. Then connect each of the two dots to the single dot.

$$5 < 8$$

Another way is to think of the open end of the symbol as a mouth swallowing the larger number.

$$5 \quad < \quad 8$$

Write <, >, or =.

Example

18 __>__ 12

< is less than
> is more than
= is the same as
= is equal to

1. 11 _____ 7   **2.** 21 _____ 25   **3.** 37 _____ 37

4. 29 _____ 42   **5.** 35 _____ 15   **6.** 48 _____ 128

Challenge

7. 16 _____ 5 + 10   **8.** 8 + 2 _____ 10

Family Note

Children are continuing to practice counting coins. The Challenge problem is difficult because the coins are not in any particular order. It might help to sort real coins into groups of like coins (all dimes together, all nickels together) before counting. To find a combination with fewer coins, exchange pennies for nickels and nickels for dimes. Many children are still learning to write amounts of money using dollars-and-cents notation. We will continue to practice this skill during the year.

Please return this Home Link to school tomorrow.

Ⓟ 1 cent	Ⓝ 5 cents	Ⓓ 10 cents
$0.01	$0.05	$0.10
a penny	a nickel	a dime

How much? Write each answer in cents and in dollars-and-cents notation.

1. Ⓓ Ⓝ Ⓝ Ⓝ Ⓝ Ⓟ Ⓟ _____¢ or $_____

2. Ⓓ Ⓝ Ⓝ Ⓝ Ⓝ Ⓝ Ⓟ _____¢ or $_____

3. Ⓓ Ⓓ Ⓝ Ⓝ Ⓝ Ⓟ Ⓟ Ⓟ _____¢ or $_____

Challenge

4. Ⓟ Ⓟ Ⓝ Ⓟ Ⓓ Ⓓ Ⓝ Ⓓ Ⓝ Ⓟ Ⓟ _____¢ or $_____

On the back of this paper show this amount with fewer coins. Use Ⓟ, Ⓝ, and Ⓓ.

Domino Addition

Family Note

Children are continuing to practice basic addition facts. Notice that we are emphasizing +0, +1, +2, and double facts like 3 + 3.

Please return this Home Link to school tomorrow.

Add.

1.
$$\begin{array}{r} 4 \\ + 4 \\ \hline \end{array}$$

2.
$$\begin{array}{r} 6 \\ + 6 \\ \hline \end{array}$$

3.
$$\begin{array}{r} 2 \\ + 2 \\ \hline \end{array}$$

4.
$$\begin{array}{r} 0 \\ + 6 \\ \hline \end{array}$$

5.   ___ = 2 + 1

6.   1 + 5 = ___

7.   3 + 3 = ___

8.   ___ = 0 + 9

Fill in the missing dots and fill in the missing numbers.

9.
$$\begin{array}{r} 4 \\ + 0 \\ \hline \\ \end{array}$$

10.
$$\begin{array}{r} 8 \\ + \underline{\quad} \\ \hline 16 \end{array}$$

11.

5 + _____ = 10

Challenge

12. Draw a domino of your choice. Write an addition fact to go with it.

_____

Relation Symbols

Family Note

As children continue their work with relation symbols, you can help at home by having your child read aloud the number models on this page. Read the example as follows: 65 is less than 83.

Please return this Home Link to school tomorrow.

Write <, >, or =.

Example 65 _____ 83

> < is less than
> > is more than
> = is the same as
> = is equal to

1. 15 _____ 17   **2.** 28 _____ 19   **3.** 24 _____ 24

4. 36 _____ 63   **5.** 72 _____ 92   **6.** 55 _____ 128

Challenge

Fill in numbers to make these correct.

7. 46 < _____   **8.** _____ > 155

Comparing Amounts of Money

Family Note

Children are beginning to work with number stories in which they find how much more (or less) one number is than another. This is called the *difference* between the two numbers. Notice that the smaller numbers in the problems are always shown in smaller frames.

Help your child line up the pennies in two rows and pair pennies in the top row with pennies in the bottom row. Have your child make as many pairs as possible. The extra pennies that could not be paired off represent the difference.

Please return this Home Link to school tomorrow.

---

1. Bart   Ⓟ Ⓟ Ⓟ Ⓟ Ⓟ Ⓟ Ⓟ Ⓟ Ⓟ Ⓟ Ⓟ Ⓟ

    Perry   Ⓟ Ⓟ Ⓟ Ⓟ Ⓟ Ⓟ Ⓟ Ⓟ

Who has more? _____   How much more? _____ ¢

---

2. Tricia   Ⓟ Ⓟ Ⓟ

    Martha   Ⓟ Ⓟ Ⓟ Ⓟ Ⓟ Ⓟ Ⓟ Ⓟ Ⓟ Ⓟ Ⓟ

Who has more? _____   How much more? _____ ¢

---

3. Franklin | 17 pennies |

    Maria | 25 pennies |

Who has more? _____   How much more? _____ ¢

---

4. Michelle | 19 pennies |

    Lawrence | 8 pennies |

Who has more? _____   How much more? _____ ¢

Number Stories

Family Note

Children have been telling and solving number stories in class. Have your child explain the number story that goes with the picture he or she chooses. If you like, help your child record the number story in words. The number model may show addition or subtraction, depending on how your child tells the story.

Please return this Home Link to school tomorrow.

Here is a number story Mandy made up.

I have 4 balloons.
Jamal brought 1 more.
We have 5 balloons together.

4 + 1 = 5

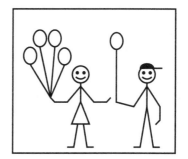

Unit
balloons

Find a picture in a magazine. Use it to write a number story or draw your own picture.

Write a number model to go with your story.

Unit

Comparing Sums

Family Note

For the next few days, children will return to the basic addition facts. They will concentrate on memorizing the +1 and + 0 facts (for example, 7 + 0 and 8 + 1), doubles facts (doubles like 3 + 3), and facts that have a sum of 10 (for example, 3 + 7 and 6 + 4). This will take time and practice. Consider spending a little bit of time each day practicing these addition facts with your child.

Please return this Home Link to school tomorrow.

Write <, >, or =.

Challenge

5.

Turn-Around Dice

Family Note

Turn-around addition facts are pairs of facts in which the numbers that are being added are the same. Turn-around facts have the same sum. For example, $2 + 3 = 5$ and $3 + 2 = 5$ are turn-around facts. Knowing about turn-around facts cuts down on the number of facts that have to be memorized: If you know a fact, you also know its turn-around fact.

Please return this Home Link to school tomorrow.

Find the total number of dots on the dice.
Watch for turn-around facts.

Unit
dice dots

1. ⚅ + ⚂

____ + ____ = ____

2. ⚂ + ⚅

____ + ____ = ____

3. ⚄
     ☐
+ ⚃
+ ☐
____

4. ⚃
     ☐
+ ⚄
+ ☐
____

Make up your own turn-around facts. Draw the dots
and write the addition facts.

5. ☐ + ☐

____ + ____ = ____

6. ☐ + ☐

____ + ____ = ____

Adding 0 and 1

Family Note

Give your child several 1-digit, 2-digit, and 3-digit numbers. Ask him or her to add 0 and 1 to each.

Use some numbers with 9 in the ones place like 9, 49, 79, 129, 359, and 789. Also use 0 in the tens and ones places, like in 208 and 320.

Please return this Home Link to school tomorrow.

1. Ask someone at home to say a 1-digit number; for example, 7. Add 0 to the number and give the answer. Then add 1 to the number and give the answer.

2. Have someone say a 2-digit or 3-digit number. Add 0 and 1 to this number.

3. Find the answers to more +0 and +1 problems with 2-digit or 3-digit numbers. Write them in the table below.

Example   25   25 + 0 = 25

$$\begin{array}{r} 25 \\ + 1 \\ \hline 26 \end{array}$$

Number Models

	Number	**+0**	**+1**
Example	25	25 + 0 = 25	25 + 1 = 26
1-digit number			
2-digit number			
3-digit number			
Your choice			

"What's My Rule?"

Today your child learned about a kind of problem you may not have seen before. We call it "What's My Rule?" Please ask your child to explain it to you.

Here is a little background information you may find useful. Imagine a machine with a funnel at the top and a tube at the bottom—we call this a *function machine*. The function machine can be programmed so that if you drop a number into the funnel at the top, the machine does something to the number according to a rule to make a new number come out of the tube at the bottom. For example, you can program the machine to add 2 to any number that is dropped into the funnel. If you put in 3, out comes 5; if you put in 6, out comes 8.

You can show this with a table:

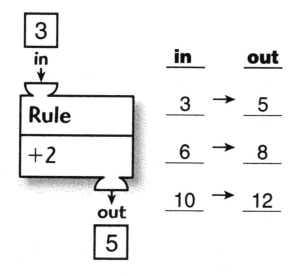

in		out
3	→	5
6	→	8
10	→	12

Here is another example of a function machine:

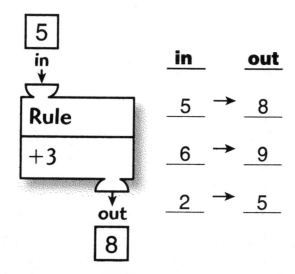

in		out
5	→	8
6	→	9
2	→	5

In a "What's My Rule?" problem, some of the information is missing. To solve the problem, you have to find the missing information. The missing information can be the numbers that come out, the numbers that are dropped in, or the rule for programming the machine. *For example:*

Missing "out" numbers

Missing rule

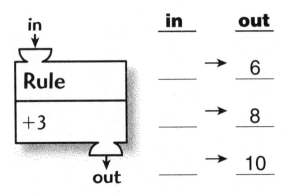

Missing "in" numbers

Use with Lesson 5.12.

"What's My Rule?"

Family Note

Ask your child to explain what the function machine is doing to the "in" numbers before filling in the missing "out" numbers. For example, in the first problem, the function machine is adding 1 to each of the "in" numbers.

   The Challenge problem may prove difficult because it does not involve addition or subtraction. However, children often have an intuitive grasp of "$\frac{1}{2}$ of a number." We will continue to provide experiences with number patterns (as well as other kinds of patterns) in future lessons.

Please return this Home Link to school tomorrow.

Fill in the missing numbers.

1.

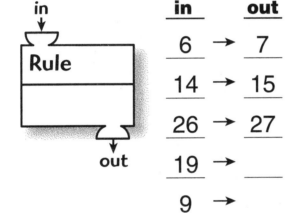

in		out
6	→	7
14	→	15
26	→	27
19	→	
9	→	

Your turn: ___ → ___

2.

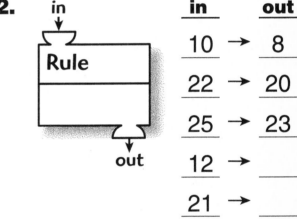

in		out
10	→	8
22	→	20
25	→	23
12	→	
21	→	

Your turn: ___ → ___

3.

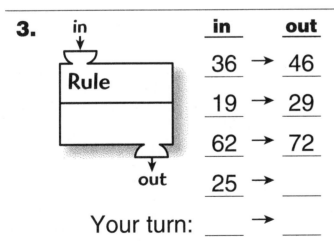

in		out
36	→	46
19	→	29
62	→	72
25	→	

Your turn: ___ → ___

Challenge

4.

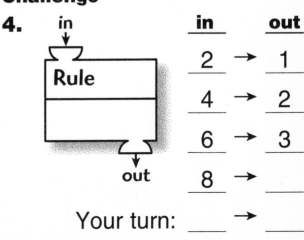

in		out
2	→	1
4	→	2
6	→	3
8	→	

Your turn: ___ → ___

More "What's My Rule?"

Family Note

Children are continuing their exploration of number patterns. Each problem on this page represents a different kind of problem.

In the first problem, your child tries to find the rule.

In the second and fourth problems, the rule is given. The second problem calls for applying the rule to find the "out" numbers; the fourth problem calls for applying the rule to find the "in" numbers. This problem is especially challenging because you must do the opposite of the rule to find the "in" numbers (subtract 2).

Encourage your child to describe how he or she solved each problem.

Please return this Home Link to school tomorrow.

1. Find the rule.

in
↓
Rule

out

in	out
5	8
10	13
18	21

Your turn: _____ | _____

2. What comes out?

in
↓
Rule
−10

out

in	out
13	3
26	
45	

Your turn: _____ | _____

3. Make your own.

in
↓
Rule

out

in	out

Challenge

4. What goes in?

in
↓
Rule
+2

out

in	out
	5
	3
	2

Your turn: _____ | _____

Unit 6: Developing Fact Power

Knowing the basic facts is as important to mathematics as knowing words by sight is to reading. Your child should start to get a good handle on many addition and subtraction facts by the end of the year.

Learning the facts takes practice. It is not necessary to practice for a long time, but it is important to practice often, almost every day. One good way to practice is to play the games that are introduced at school. (See the third page of this letter.)

In Unit 6, children will learn shortcuts that will make it easier to learn the facts. One shortcut is the turn-around rule, which simply states that the order in which numbers are added does not change the sum. For example, 3 + 4 and 4 + 3 both equal 7, so when your child has learned one of these facts, he or she automatically knows its turn-around fact. Your child will also learn how easy it is to add 0 and 1 to any number. Working with shortcuts like these will help build "fact power."

Also, children will broaden their money skills by counting coins that include quarters.

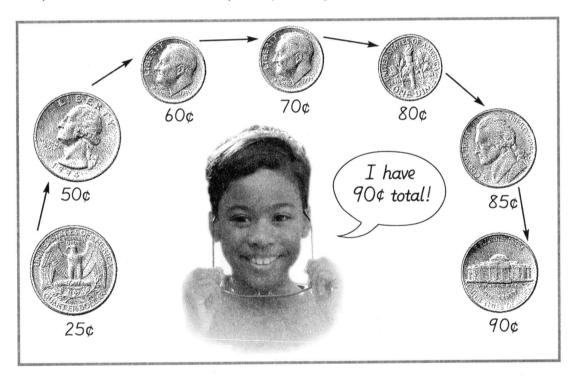

Later in this unit, children will extend their time-telling skills by learning to tell time to the nearest 5 minutes and by representing the time in digital notation, as it appears on a digital clock.

Please keep this letter for reference as your child works through Unit 6.

Math Tools

Your child will be using **Fact Triangles** to practice and review addition and subtraction facts. Fact Triangles are a "new and improved" version of flash cards; the addition and subtraction facts shown are made from the same three numbers, and this helps your child understand the relationships among those facts. The *Family Note* on Home Link 6.4, which you will receive later, provides a more detailed description of Fact Triangles.

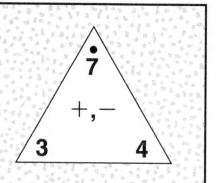

Vocabulary

Important terms in Unit 6:

addition and subtraction facts The addition facts are the 100 possible combinations of two one-digit addends. The subtraction facts are the inverses of the addition facts.

fact family A group of addition facts together with the subtraction facts. For example, the following facts form the fact family for the numbers 3, 4, and 7:

$$3 + 4 = 7$$
$$4 + 3 = 7$$
$$7 - 3 = 4$$
$$7 - 4 = 3$$

function machine A diagram of an imaginary machine programmed to process numbers according to a certain rule. A number (input) is put into the machine and is transformed into a second number (output) through the application of a rule.

name-collection box A boxlike diagram tagged with a given number and used for collecting equivalent names for that number.

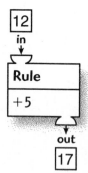

digital clock A clock that uses only numbers to show the time in hours and minutes, with a colon used to separate them.

range The difference between the greatest and least numbers in a set of data. For example, in the set of data below, the difference between 36 and 28 is 8, so 8 is the range.

middle value The number in the middle when a set of data is organized in sequential order. For example, in the following set of data, 32 is the middle value:

$$28 \ 28 \ 31 \ 32 \ 33 \ 35 \ 36$$

"What's My Rule?" A routine that consists of a set of number pairs in which the numbers in each pair are related to each other according to the same rule. The problems are usually displayed in a table format, in which two of the three parts are known. The goal is to find the unknown part.

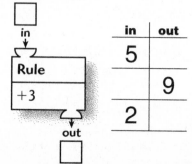

Building Skills through Games

In Unit 6, your child will practice addition, subtraction, and place-value skills by playing the following games.

Beat the Calculator

A "Calculator" (a player who uses a calculator) and a "Brain" (a player who solves the problem without a calculator) race to see who will be first to solve addition problems.

Difference Game

Players pick a card and collect as many pennies as the number shown on the card. Then players count each other's pennies and figure out how many more pennies one player has than the other.

Tens-and-Ones Trading Game

Players take turns putting base-10 blocks on their Tens-and-Ones Mat according to the roll of a die. Whenever possible, they exchange 10 cubes for 1 long. The first player to get to 10 longs wins!

Do-Anytime Activities

To work with your child on the concepts taught in this unit and in previous units, try these interesting and rewarding activities:

1. Using the Fact Triangles, cover the sum for addition practice. Cover one of the other numbers for subtraction practice. Make this brief and fun.

2. Have your child tell you a number story that fits a given number model, such as $3 + 5 = 8$.

3. Go to your local library and check out the book *12 Ways to Get to 11* by Eve Merriam, an entertaining book that presents addition facts.

4. Play with name-collection boxes. Begin with a number, such as 20, and find at least five equivalent names for the number.

Use with Lesson 5.14.

As You Help Your Child with Homework

As your child brings home assignments, you may want to go over the instructions together, clarifying them as necessary. The answers listed below will guide you through this unit's Home Links.

Home Link 6.3

1. 5, 7, 12; 5 + 7 = 12; 7 + 5 = 12; 12 − 5 = 7; 12 − 7 = 5

2. 6, 9, 15; 6 + 9 = 15; 9 + 6 = 15; 15 − 6 = 9; 15 − 9 = 6

3. 8, 8, 16; 8 + 8 = 16; 16 − 8 = 8

Home Link 6.5

1. 3, 9, 12; 3 + 9 = 12; 9 + 3 = 12; 12 − 3 = 9; 12 − 9 = 3

3.

Home Link 6.8

3. George Washington; 25 Ⓟ; 25¢; 5 Ⓝ

Home Link 6.9

1. 50¢, or $0.50 **2.** 82¢, or $0.82

3. 43¢, or $0.43 **4.** 72¢, or $0.72

5. 121¢, or $1.21

Home Link 6.10

1.

2.

3.

Home Link 6.12

1. 25 **2.** 18

3. 5 **4.** 13

Use with Lesson 5.14.

Using the Addition Table

Family Note

Children are continuing to practice addition facts in class. Today they learned how to use the facts table to help find sums. Children used sheets of paper and lined them up as illustrated at the right.

+, −	0	1	2	3	4	5	6	7	8	9
0	0	1	2	3	4	5	6	7	8	9
1	1	2	3	4	5	6	7	8	9	10
2	2	3	4	5	6	7	8	9	10	11
3	3	4	5	6	7	8	9	10	11	12
4	4	5	6	7	8	9	10	11	12	13
5	5	6	7	8	9	10	11	12	13	14
6	6	7	8	9	10	11	12	13	14	15
7	7	8	9	10	11	12	13	14	15	16
8	8	9	10	11	12	13	14	15	16	17
9	9	10	11	12	13	14	15	16	17	18

Help your child find sums in the table. It is OK to solve the problems using other strategies, such as counting on or using counters to model the problems.

Please return this Home Link to school tomorrow.

Using the Addition Table (cont.)

Use the color code to color the picture.

Color Code

10 = green   14 = yellow
12 = blue   15 = red

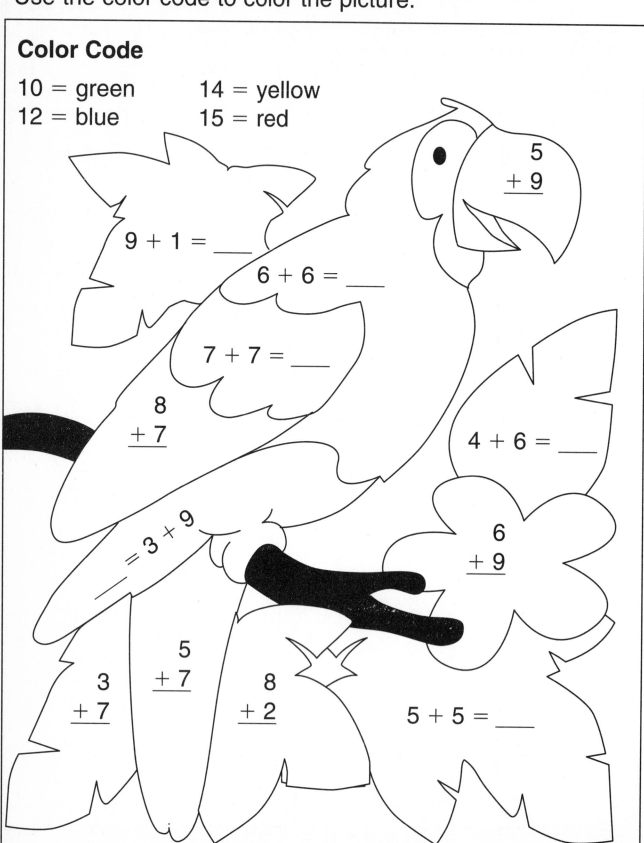

$9 + 1 =$ ___

$6 + 6 =$ ___

$7 + 7 =$ ___

$\begin{array}{r} 5 \\ + 9 \\ \hline \end{array}$

$\begin{array}{r} 8 \\ + 7 \\ \hline \end{array}$

$4 + 6 =$ ___

___ $= 3 + 9$

$\begin{array}{r} 6 \\ + 9 \\ \hline \end{array}$

$\begin{array}{r} 5 \\ + 7 \\ \hline \end{array}$

$\begin{array}{r} 3 \\ + 7 \\ \hline \end{array}$

$\begin{array}{r} 8 \\ + 2 \\ \hline \end{array}$

$5 + 5 =$ ___

146

Family Note

Today, we began working with name-collection boxes. See the attached letter for more information about this routine.

Please return this Home Link to school tomorrow.

List all the addition facts you know that have a sum of 10.

_____

_____

Write as many names as you can in the name-collection boxes.

15	18

10 + 5

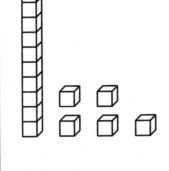

Name-Collection Boxes

People, things, and ideas often have several different names. For example, Mary calls her parents Mom and Dad. Other people in the family may call them Linda and John, or Aunt Linda and Uncle John, or Grandma and Grandpa. Mail may come addressed to Mr. and Mrs. West. All are names for the same two people.

Your child is bringing home an activity that has a special format for using this naming idea with numbers. We call the format a name-collection box. The box is used for collecting many names for given numbers.

This format offers a simple way for children to understand the idea that numbers can be expressed in many different ways. The open-top box is identified by the name on the label. The box shown here is a 25-box, a name-collection box for the number 25.

Names can include sums, differences, products, quotients, or combinations of operations, as well as words (including words in other languages), tallies, and arrays. A name-collection box can be filled by using any equivalent names.

With repeated practice, children gain the power to rename numbers for a variety of different uses.

25
37 − 12   20 + 5
twenty-five
veinticinco   X X X X X
X X X X X
X X X X X
X X X X X
X X X X X

25-box

Fact Families

Family Note

We have extended our work with facts to subtraction facts by introducing fact families. Your child will generate addition facts and subtraction facts to go with the numbers pictured on the dominoes below.

Note that for the first two problems, there are two addition facts and two subtraction facts. Because the third problem shows a domino with the same number on both halves, there is only one addition fact and one subtraction fact. Ask your child to explain why this is the case.

Please return this Home Link to school tomorrow.

Write the 3 numbers for each domino. Use the numbers to write the fact family.

1. Numbers: _____, _____, _____

Fact family: ____ + ____ = ____   ____ − ____ = ____

____ + ____ = ____   ____ − ____ = ____

2. Numbers: _____, _____, _____

Fact family: ____ + ____ = ____   ____ − ____ = ____

____ + ____ = ____   ____ − ____ = ____

3. Numbers: _____, _____, _____

Fact family: ____ + ____ = ____   ____ − ____ = ____

Fact Triangles

Your child should cut apart the triangles on the other page. Notice that each triangle has the three numbers used in a fact family on it. Use these triangles like flash cards to practice addition and subtraction facts.

The number below the dot is the sum of the other two numbers. For example, 8 is the sum of 5 and 3.

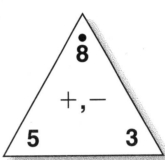

To practice addition, cover the sum. Your child then adds the numbers that are not covered. For example, if you cover 8, your child adds 5 and 3.

To practice subtraction, cover one of the numbers at the bottom of the triangle. Your child then subtracts the uncovered number at the bottom from the sum. For example, if you cover 3, your child subtracts 5 from 8. If you cover 5, your child subtracts 3 from 8.

Fact Triangles have two advantages over regular flash cards.

1. They reinforce the strong link between addition and subtraction.

2. They help simplify the memorizing task by linking four facts together. Knowing a single fact means that you really know four facts.

$$5 + 3 = 8$$
$$3 + 5 = 8$$
$$8 - 5 = 3$$
$$8 - 3 = 5$$

Save this set of Fact Triangles in an envelope or a plastic bag to continue practicing addition and subtraction facts with your child when you have time.

Fact Triangles

Cut out the 6 triangles. Practice the addition and subtraction facts on these triangles with someone at home.

Fact Routines Practice

Family Note

This Home Link reviews some of the work children have been doing in recent lessons. Note that children are now working with subtraction facts as they are related to addition facts. Encourage your child to include some subtraction "names" in the name-collection box in Problem 3. An example of a subtraction name for the first name-collection-box is *16 − 2*.

Please return this Home Link to school tomorrow.

Write the 3 numbers for the domino. Use the numbers to write the fact family.

1. Numbers: _____, _____, _____

Fact family: ____ + ____ = ____   ____ − ____ = ____

____ + ____ = ____   ____ − ____ = ____

2. Write as many names as you can for 14.

14

3. Cross out the names that do not belong.

20
10 + 10   twenty
~~卌 卌~~   5 + 5 + 5
2 + 10   15 + 1
20 + 0
24 − 4

Measuring in Centimeters

Home Link
6.6

Cut out the ruler. Find four small objects. Draw a picture of each object and measure each object to the nearest centimeter (cm). Record your measurements.

1.	2.
About _____ cm long	About _____ cm long
3.	4.
About _____ cm long	About _____ cm long

Practicing with Fact Triangles

Family Note

Six more Fact Triangles are being added for practice at home. As you help your child practice with the Fact Triangles, keep the facts your child knows in a separate pile from the facts that still need some work.

Please return this Home Link to school tomorrow.

Cut out the Fact Triangles. Practice these facts at home when you have time. When you are not using the triangles, store them in an envelope or a plastic bag.

Counting Coins

Family Note

This Home Link reviews counting combinations of dimes, nickels, and pennies. If your child is having trouble counting coins, you might try the following method:

1. First show the amount with pennies.

2. Then trade the pennies for nickels.

3. Finally, trade the nickels for dimes.

Use real coins if possible.
Children are adding quarters to their work with coins, beginning tomorrow. In preparation for this, please give your child two quarters to bring to school.

Please return this Home Link to school tomorrow.

Use Ⓟ, Ⓝ, and Ⓓ to show each of the amounts in two different ways.

1. 43¢

| | |
| | |

2. 67¢

| | |
| | |

3. Ask someone at home for a quarter.

Who is on the HEADS side? _____

Complete.

1 quarter = _____ Ⓟ   1 quarter = _____ ¢

1 quarter = _____ Ⓝ

More Counting Coins

Family Note

Children have begun to count coin combinations that include quarters. If your child is having difficulty because the coins are not shown in any particular order, use real coins to model the problems. Sort the coins into groups of like coins (all dimes together, all nickels together) before counting.

Children are also continuing to use dollars-and-cents notation. If your child has trouble recording amounts in this notation, don't worry—this is a skill we will continue to work on throughout the year.

Please return this Home Link to school tomorrow.

Ⓟ	Ⓝ	Ⓓ	Ⓠ
1¢	5¢	10¢	25¢
$0.01	$0.05	$0.10	$0.25

Count the coins.

Write the total in cents and in dollars-and-cents notation.

1. Ⓠ Ⓓ Ⓝ Ⓝ Ⓝ _____¢ or $_____

2. Ⓠ Ⓠ Ⓓ Ⓓ Ⓝ Ⓝ Ⓟ Ⓟ _____¢ or $_____

3. Ⓓ Ⓟ Ⓝ Ⓟ Ⓟ Ⓠ _____¢ or $_____

4. Ⓟ Ⓝ Ⓝ Ⓠ Ⓟ Ⓠ Ⓓ _____¢ or $_____

Challenge

5. Ⓟ Ⓠ Ⓠ Ⓝ Ⓓ Ⓓ Ⓝ Ⓝ Ⓠ Ⓓ _____¢ or $_____

Time at 5-Minute Intervals

Family Note

In today's lesson children started to work with digital displays of time. Children talked about the number of minutes in an hour and started to tell time at 5-minute intervals. This will require lots of practice, so the *Everyday Mathematics* program will come back to telling time throughout the year.

Please return this Home Link to school tomorrow.

Draw the hour hand and the minute hand.

1.

4:00

2.

7:30

3.

10:15

4. Make up your own.

_____:_____

More Fact Triangles

Family Note

Your child should cut out the triangles on this page. When not using the triangles, store them in the envelope or plastic bag with the first 12 triangles from earlier lessons. As you work with your child, keep a pile of the facts your child knows and a second pile of the facts that still need some work.

Continue practicing addition and subtraction facts at home when you have time.

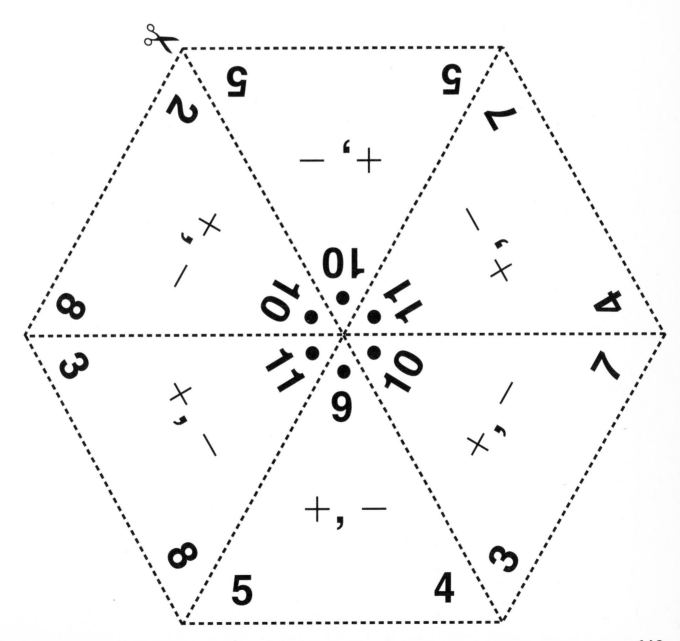

Name _____ Date _____

Analyzing a Set of Data

Family Note

Today, we did some calculator counts in class. Ask your child what his or her highest count was at the end of 15 seconds.

Below is a tally chart like one we made in class today. Help your child identify the lowest and the highest counts that someone in Casey's class got. Then help your child find the range of all the counts. (To find the range, subtract the lowest count from the highest count.)

Please return this Home Link to school tomorrow.

Casey's Class Data for Calculator Counts

Counted to	Number of Children
5	/
7	//
10	////
11	//// /
12	////
13	///
15	//
17	/
18	/

1. How many children in Casey's class did the calculator count?

_____

2. Find the highest count.

_____

3. Find the lowest count.

_____

4. Find the range of the counts.

_____

5. If you have a calculator, show someone at home how you did the calculator count. Ask that person to count on the calculator.

Family Letter

Unit 7: Geometry and Attributes

In Unit 7, children will work with 2-dimensional shapes. First, children will classify blocks by their shape, color, and size. Then they will learn to recognize attributes like number of sides and square corners. Later, they will build their own shapes out of straws and twist-ties, identifying the differences among shapes that are polygons and shapes that are not.

Children will work with 3-dimensional shapes they encounter every day. They will be asked to bring objects from home, which will be organized and labeled to create a "Shapes Museum" for the classroom. For example, a soup can would be labeled "cylinder"; a tennis ball, "sphere." In examining the shapes brought to class, children will begin to identify similarities and differences among five kinds of 3-dimensional shapes: prisms, pyramids, spheres, cylinders, and cones. They will learn to identify characteristics, using terms like *flat* and *round*. We will use the names of the shapes in class, but children will not be expected to memorize their definitions.

In the last lesson of this unit, children will explore symmetry. They will find symmetrical shapes in real life, including butterflies, bells, guitars, vases, and double dominoes. Then they will create their own symmetrical shapes using paper and scissors.

Please keep this Family Letter for reference as your child works through Unit 7.

2-Dimensional Shapes

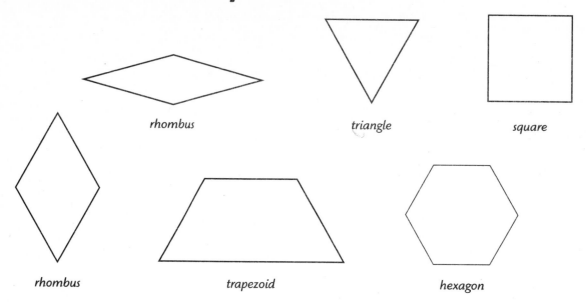

rhombus   *triangle*   *square*

rhombus   *trapezoid*   *hexagon*

3-Dimensional Shapes

 prism A shape with two parallel flat faces (bases) that are the same size and shape. Prisms are classified according to the shape of their two parallel bases. The other sides (also called *faces*) are parallelograms. (A parallelogram is a four-sided polygon with two pairs of parallel sides.) Examples of prisms include books, cereal boxes, and bricks.

pyramid A shape in which one face (the base) is a polygon and the other faces are triangles with a common vertex (corner). (A polygon is a 2-dimensional shape consisting of straight sides that meet only at their ends.) Architectural examples of pyramids include the Transamerica Building in San Francisco, the Temple of the Sun in Peru, and the Pyramids in Egypt.

 sphere A shape with a curved surface that is, at all points, the same distance from its center point. A ball is shaped like a sphere.

cylinder A shape with a curved surface and two parallel, circular faces (bases) that are the same size. Examples of cylinders include empty paper towel rolls, coffee cans, and fluorescent lightbulbs.

 cone A shape with a curved surface, a circular face (base), and one vertex (corner). Examples of cones include cone-shaped party hats, sugar cones served with ice cream, and the orange cones commonly used in road construction.

Use with Lesson 6.13.

Do-Anytime Activities

To work with your child on the concepts taught in this unit and in previous units, try these interesting and rewarding activities:

1 Draw a name-collection box with a number on the tag. Ask your child to write at least 10 equivalent names for the given number.

2 Occasionally ask questions about time: What time is it? What time will it be in five minutes? In ten minutes? In one hour?

3 Continue to work on addition and subtraction facts using Fact Triangles, short drill sessions, and any of the games introduced at school.

4 If a calculator is available, ask your child to show you how to count with it. See how high your child can count on the calculator.

12
17 − 5
2 + 10
4 + 8
13 − 1
twelve
doce
⫫⫫ ⫫⫫ ‖

5 Look for geometric shapes around the house, at the supermarket, as part of architectural features, and on street signs. Begin to call these shapes by their geometric names.

Building Skills through Games

In Unit 7, your child will practice place-value and classification skills by playing the following games:

Attribute Train Game

One player puts down a block. The next player finds a block that differs in only one attribute—shape, size, or color—from the first block and puts it next to the first block. Each player continues to add to the "train" of blocks.

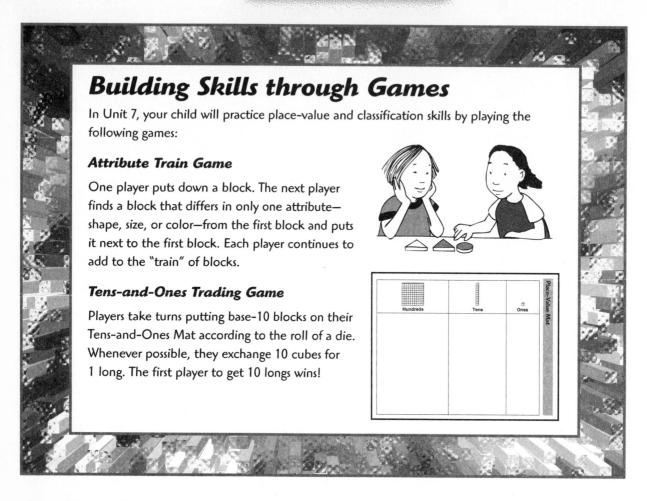

Tens-and-Ones Trading Game

Players take turns putting base-10 blocks on their Tens-and-Ones Mat according to the roll of a die. Whenever possible, they exchange 10 cubes for 1 long. The first player to get 10 longs wins!

As You Help Your Child with Homework

As your child brings home assignments, you may want to go over the instructions together, clarifying them as necessary. The answers listed below will guide you through this unit's Home Links.

Home Link 7.3

square

rhombus

hexagon

trapezoid

triangle

rhombus

Home Link 7.4

1.

2. Sample drawing:

3. Sample drawing:

Use with Lesson 6.13.

Family Note

Your child should cut apart the Fact Triangles on this page. Add these to the envelope or plastic bag with the Fact Triangles from earlier lessons. As you show the triangles, put the facts your child knows in one pile, and the facts that still need work in another pile.

Cut out these Fact Triangles.

Practice the facts at home.

Shapes

Family Note

The class has been identifying and comparing three attributes of objects: shape, color, and size. We are going to work with 2-dimensional and 3-dimensional shapes in future lessons. In preparation for this, help your child find objects with the shapes listed. Also help your child find things to bring to school for our Shapes Museum. They should not be valuable or breakable.

Please return this Home Link to school tomorrow.

1. Find something in your house that has a triangle in it. Write its name or draw its picture.

2. Find something in your house that has a circle in it. Write its name or draw its picture.

3. Find something in your house that has a square in it. Write its name or draw its picture.

4. Starting tomorrow, bring things to school for the Shapes Museum. You might bring in boxes, soup cans, balls, party hats, pyramids, and any other shapes you can find. Get permission to bring things that are not yours.

Family Note

We are beginning to identify polygons and their characteristics. In today's lesson, we made designs with blocks shaped like the polygons on this page.

On this page, your child will try to name the shapes we worked with today. Expect that some of the names may still be confusing. Help your child find designs at home that repeat the shapes on this page; for example, floor tiles repeat a square over and over again.

Please return this Home Link to school tomorrow.

Use the word bank to help you write the name for each shape.

Word Bank				
hexagon	rhombus	square	trapezoid	triangle

_____   _____   _____

_____   _____   _____

Find patterns or repeating designs at home that have pattern-block shapes in them. Draw one of these patterns or designs on the back of this page.

Write where you found this pattern. Have someone help you.

Identifying Polygons

Family Note

This Home Link follows up our work in class identifying shapes called polygons. The sides of a polygon are all straight. Polygons have corners where two sides meet. Sides meet only at their ends. The sides are connected—there aren't any gaps. Help your child identify the polygons below.

Please return this Home Link to school tomorrow.

1. Circle all the shapes below that are polygons.

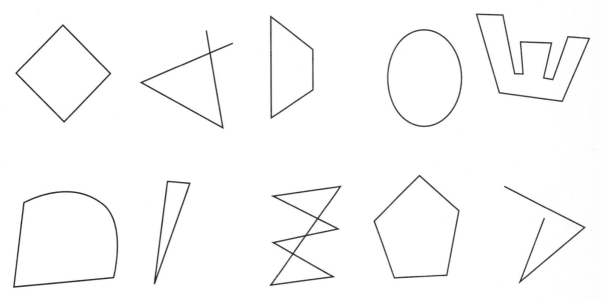

Challenge

2. Draw a shape that is NOT on this page, and IS a polygon.

3. Draw a shape that is NOT on this page, and IS NOT a polygon.

Practicing with Fact Triangles

Family Note Your child should cut apart the triangles on this page. Add these to the envelope or plastic bag with the Fact Triangles from earlier lessons. As you show the triangles, make a pile of the facts your child knows and a second pile of the facts that still need work.

Continue practicing addition and subtraction facts at home.

Family Note

The class has been working with 2-dimensional and 3-dimensional shapes. For today's Home Link, help your child find 3-dimensional objects, and then help him or her trace around one surface of each object—for example, the bottom of a box, the bottom of a can, the bottom of a cup, and so on. Use the front and back of this sheet, and other sheets if you want. For each tracing, help your child find a name for the shape in the Word Bank, and write the name on the tracing.

Please return this Home Link to school tomorrow.

Find 3-dimensional shapes with flat faces (sides).

On the front and back of this page trace around one face of each shape.

Write the name of the shape.

Word Bank
square
trapezoid
not a polygon
circle
rhombus
rectangle
hexagon
triangle
other polygon

Finding Symmetry in Nature

Family Note

A picture or object has symmetry if it can be folded in half so that the two halves match exactly. In today's lesson, the class explored symmetry by cutting out designs from folded paper. To continue our exploration of symmetry, help your child find pictures that show symmetry in nature. For example: pictures of butterflies, leaves, animal markings, flowers, snowflakes, and so on.

Please return this Home Link to school tomorrow.

Find symmetrical pictures in magazines.

Cut out your favorite pictures and glue them onto this page.

Unit 8: **Mental Arithmetic, Money, and Fractions**

In Unit 8, children will examine a dollar bill and add the dollar to the money units they already know. They will continue to count and record amounts of money (using pennies, nickels, dimes, and quarters), often in more than one way. They will also begin learning how to make change.

Children will also create addition, subtraction, and comparison problems for the class to solve and will share their own problem-solving strategies. Having children share their solution strategies is emphasized in *Everyday Mathematics* and helps children feel more confident as they express their ideas.

Later in this unit, children will work with fractions. They will be reminded that fractions are equal parts of wholes. When dealing with fractions, it is important that children keep in mind the "whole" or the ONE to which the fraction is linked. For example, $\frac{1}{2}$ of an apple and $\frac{1}{2}$ of a dollar are not the same, because they deal with different types of "wholes."

$\frac{7}{12}$ *of my creature is blue.*

Please keep this Family Letter for reference as your child works through Unit 8.

Vocabulary

Important terms in Unit 8:

fractional parts Equal parts of any whole.
For example:

Half ($\frac{1}{2}$) of the objects that make
up a whole set are broken.

One of three parts ($\frac{1}{3}$)
of a whole has been eaten.

near doubles A strategy derived from the "doubles"
facts. For example, a child might solve 3 + 4 by noting
that 3 + 3 = 6, so 3 + 4 must be 1 more than 6.

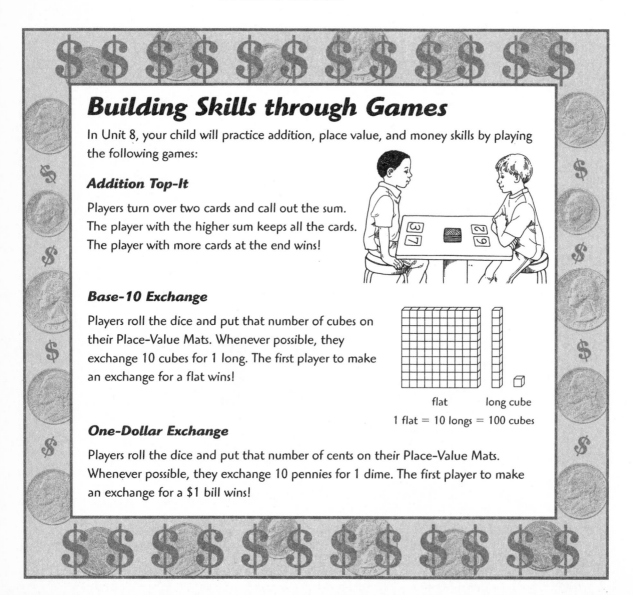

Building Skills through Games

In Unit 8, your child will practice addition, place value, and money skills by playing
the following games:

Addition Top-It

Players turn over two cards and call out the sum.
The player with the higher sum keeps all the cards.
The player with more cards at the end wins!

Base-10 Exchange

Players roll the dice and put that number of cubes on
their Place-Value Mats. Whenever possible, they
exchange 10 cubes for 1 long. The first player to make
an exchange for a flat wins!

flat   long cube
1 flat = 10 longs = 100 cubes

One-Dollar Exchange

Players roll the dice and put that number of cents on their Place-Value Mats.
Whenever possible, they exchange 10 pennies for 1 dime. The first player to make
an exchange for a $1 bill wins!

Use with Lesson 7.8.

Do-Anytime Activities

To work with your child on the concepts taught in this unit and in previous units, try these interesting and rewarding activities:

1 Continue to review addition and subtraction facts.

2 Ask questions like the following:

▶ I want to buy an airplane that costs 27 cents. If I give the clerk 3 dimes, how much change will I get back?

▶ How can you show 14 cents using exactly 6 coins? (Have the actual coins available.)

▶ How many different ways can you show 14 cents? (Have the actual coins available.)

3 Count out 8 pennies (or any type of counter, such as beans or macaroni). Ask your child to show you $\frac{1}{2}$ of the pennies and then $\frac{1}{4}$ of the pennies. Do this with a variety of different numbers.

4 Encourage your child to count various collections of coins you may have accumulated.

As You Help Your Child with Homework

As your child brings home assignments, you may want to go over the instructions together, clarifying them as necessary. The answers listed below will guide you through this unit's Home Links.

Home Link 8.1

3. September: 52¢, or $0.52

October: 61¢, or $0.61

November: 96¢, or $0.96

December: 88¢, or $0.88

4. 297¢, or $2.97

Home Link 8.2

3. 81¢, or $0.81   **4.** 125¢, or $1.25

Home Link 8.3

1. 569   **2.** 843   **3.** 709

4. 465   **5.** Answers vary.

Home Link 8.5

1. 3 dimes; 4 cents in change

2. 8 dimes; 7 cents in change

3. 10 dimes; 5 cents in change

Home Link 8.7

1.

2.   **3.**

Home Link 8.8

1. 5   **2.** 4   **3.** 4

Home Link 8.9

1. $4 + 6 = 10$

2. $9 + 1 = 10$

3. $9 + 9 = 18$

4. $3 + 7 = 10$

$7 + 3 = 10$

$10 - 3 = 7$

$10 - 7 = 3$

5. $4 + 4 = 8$

$8 - 4 = 4$

6. $1 + 6 = 7$

$6 + 1 = 7$

$7 - 1 = 6$

$7 - 6 = 1$

Coin Combinations

Family Note

In the next lesson, we will extend our work with money to include dollars. In preparation for this, we have been practicing counting coins. If your child has difficulty with some problems on this page, use real coins to model the situations. Arrange the coins into groups of like coins and count the coins of the highest value first.

Please return this Home Link to school tomorrow.

1. Mark the coins you need to buy an eraser.

2. Mark the coins you need to buy a box of crayons.

Coin Combinations (cont.)

3. Melanie saved her money. How much did she save each month?

September

Total: _____

October

Total: _____

November

Total: _____

December

Total: _____

Challenge

4. How much did Melanie save in all? _____

Name _____   Date _____

Dollars and More

Family Note

Today we took a close look at a dollar bill. Since we have only begun to work with dollars, some of the problems on this page may be difficult for your child. If possible, use real money to model the problems. Start by counting the bills and coins in the example with your child.

Please return this Home Link to school tomorrow.

Show how you would pay for each item. Use $1, Ⓟ, Ⓝ, Ⓓ, or Ⓠ.

Example

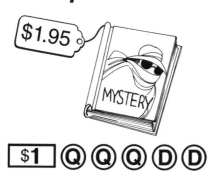

$1.95

MYSTERY

$1 Ⓠ Ⓠ Ⓠ Ⓓ Ⓓ

1.

$2.85

2.

$3.24

3. Write this amount in two ways.

Ⓠ Ⓠ Ⓝ Ⓓ Ⓝ Ⓓ Ⓟ

Total: _____ $_____.

On the back of the page, show this amount with different coins.

Challenge

4. Ⓝ Ⓓ Ⓓ Ⓓ Ⓝ Ⓓ Ⓠ Ⓠ Ⓠ

Total: _____ $_____

Name _____ Date _____

More Riddles

Home Link 8.3

Family Note

We are extending our work with base-10 blocks to include 100s. The base-10 block for 100 is called a "flat." Note that the blocks are not always shown in the same order. If your child finds some of the problems difficult, you might model them with dollar bills (for flats), dimes (for longs), and pennies (for cubes). These make good substitutes for base-10 blocks. Ask your child to explain why there is a zero in the number in Problem 3. To practice reading 3-digit numbers, ask your child to read his or her answers to you.

Please return this Home Link to school tomorrow.

Hundreds	**Tens**	**Ones**

Solve the riddles. *Example*

2 s 5 s 7 s   What am I? __257__

1. 5 s 6 s 9 s   What am I? _____

2.   4 s 8 s 3 s   What am I? _____

3. 7 hundreds and 9 ones.   What am I? _____

Challenge

4. 3 hundreds, 16 tens, 5 ones.   What am I? _____

5. Make up your own riddle. Ask someone at home to solve it.

Use with Lesson 8.3.   **199**

A Shopping Story

Family Note

We have been practicing addition of 2-digit numbers with number stories about money. Please help your child find pictures of two items in a magazine, newspaper, or catalog that each cost less than one dollar. (Newspaper inserts tend to be a good source for such items.) Ask your child to make up and tell you a number story to go with the items.

Please return this Home Link to school tomorrow.

Sample Story

I bought a ball and an eraser. I paid 52 cents.

Number model $35¢ + 17¢ = 52¢$

Glue or tape your pictures below or on the back of this page. Write your story.

Number model _____

Making Change

Family Note

Children are beginning to learn to make change. If you have dimes, nickels, and pennies available, have your child act out the problems with real money. For each problem, your child should pay with just enough dimes to cover the cost.

Please return this Home Link to school tomorrow.

Record the number of dimes you paid. Record the amount of change you got.

Example	**1.**	**2.**
marbles	balloon	toy car

I paid with

5 dimes.

I got **3** cents
in change.

I paid with

_____ dimes.

I got _____ cents
in change.

I paid with

_____ dimes.

I got _____ cents
in change.

Challenge

3. I paid with _____ dimes.

   I got _____ cents in change.

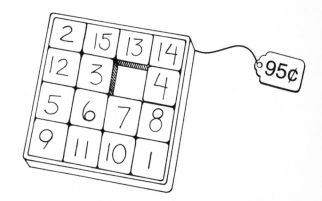

Exploring Halves and Fourths

Family Note

We are beginning to explore the concept of fractions. Today, children focused on identifying fractional parts of things. We emphasized that fractional parts come from dividing something into equal parts.

Help your child collect the items listed below.

Please return this Home Link to school tomorrow.

1. Fill a glass so that it is about half full. Then fill another glass of the same size so that it is about half empty. Is there a difference? _____

2. Divide each of the squares in half. Try to divide each square in a different way.

3. Divide each of the squares into fourths. Try to divide each square in a different way.

4. Bring one-half of something to school tomorrow. Some examples: one-half of an apple, one-half of a sandwich, one-half of a leaf, one-half of a newspaper page.

5. Also, bring one-fourth of something.

Equal Parts

Family Note

Ask your child to explain how he or she knows which figures are divided into equal fractional parts. Then help your child write fractions in the equal parts.

Please return this Home Link to school tomorrow.

Fill in the ovals below the shapes that show equal parts.
Write fractions in the equal parts.

1.

halves

       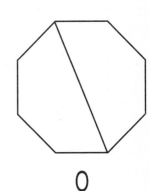

O   O   O

2.

sixths

       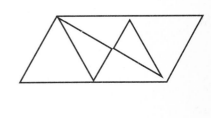

O   O   O

3.

fourths

       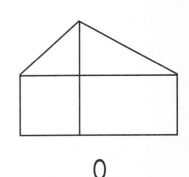

O   O   O

Name _____   Date _____

Family Note

Today we extended our work with fractions to finding fractional parts of a collection of objects. Help your child act out the problems below with pennies or counters. When sharing things equally, one strategy is to distribute the things just as you would deal cards in a card game, and then count the things in one share. In Problem 4, your child should recognize that if 15 pennies are shared equally by 6 children, there will be 3 leftover pennies.

Please return this Home Link to school tomorrow.

Use pennies to help you solve the problems.

1. Halves: 2 people share 10 pennies equally.
Circle each person's share.

Ⓟ Ⓟ Ⓟ Ⓟ Ⓟ Ⓟ Ⓟ Ⓟ Ⓟ Ⓟ

How many pennies does each person get? _____

2. Thirds: 3 children share 12 balloons equally.
Draw the balloons each child gets.

How many balloons does each child get? _____

3. Fourths: 4 children share 16 flowers equally.
How many flowers does each child get? _____

Challenge

4. Explain to someone at home what happens if 6 children share 15 pennies equally.

Facts Practice

> **Family Note**
>
> Continue to practice simple addition facts at home. The goal is for your child to memorize the + 0, + 1, doubles facts, and sums that equal 10 by the end of this school year.
>
> *Please return this Home Link to school tomorrow.*

Fill in the missing numbers.

1.

___ + 6 = ___

2.

___ + 1 = ___

3.

___ + ___ = ___

Write the fact family below each triangle.

4.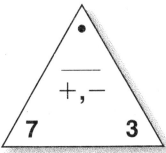

___ + ___ = ___

___ + ___ = ___

___ − ___ = ___

___ − ___ = ___

5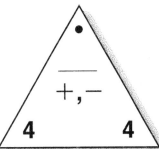

___ + ___ = ___

___ + ___ = ___

___ − ___ = ___

___ − ___ = ___

6.

___ + ___ = ___

___ + ___ = ___

___ − ___ = ___

___ − ___ = ___

Unit 9: Place Value and Fractions

The concept of place value (ones, tens, hundreds, and so on) that children have worked on since *Kindergarten Everyday Mathematics* will be taught on a more formal level in this unit. Patterns on number grids will be used to reinforce place-value concepts. For example, children may be asked to identify a hidden number on the number grid and to describe the strategies used to find and name that number. Once they are able to do this, they will solve number-grid puzzles, which are pieces of a number grid with all but a few numbers missing. Here are a few examples of number-grid puzzles:

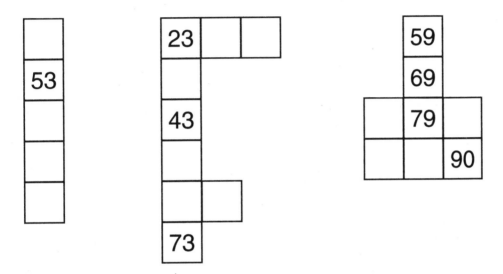

Children know that all numbers are written with one or more of only 10 digits: 0, 1, 2, 3, 4, 5, 6, 7, 8, and 9. In order to reinforce this understanding, children will identify the place value of the different digits in 2- and 3-digit numbers. Help your child remember that these same digits are also used to express quantities less than 1 with decimals or fractions.

Later in this unit, children will extend their understanding of fraction concepts as they see relationships among fraction words, meanings, and symbols.

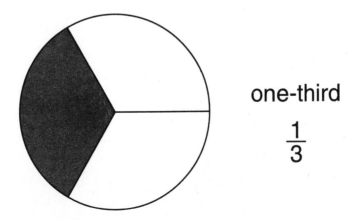

one-third

$\frac{1}{3}$

Vocabulary

Important terms in Unit 9:

numerator and **denominator** Parts of a fraction.

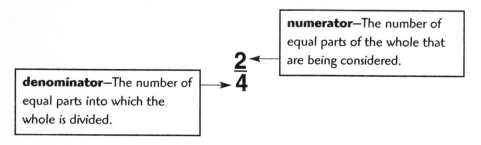

numerator—The number of equal parts of the whole that are being considered.

denominator—The number of equal parts into which the whole is divided.

2-digit numbers Numbers from 10 through 99 have two digits each.

3-digit numbers Numbers from 100 through 999 have three digits each.

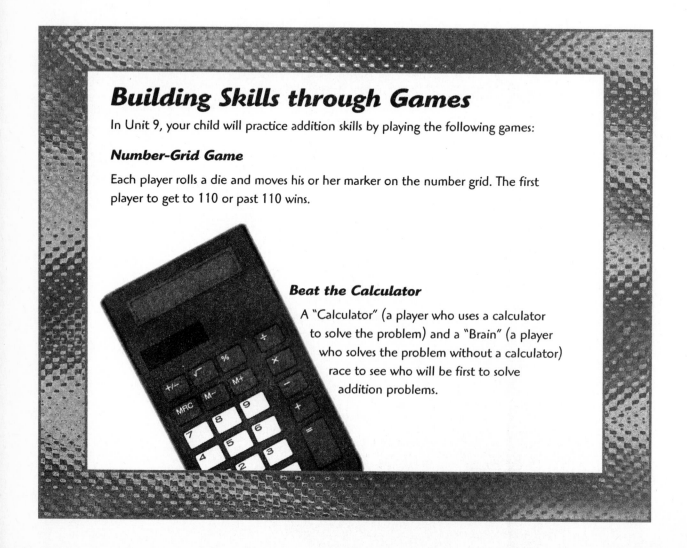

Building Skills through Games

In Unit 9, your child will practice addition skills by playing the following games:

Number-Grid Game

Each player rolls a die and moves his or her marker on the number grid. The first player to get to 110 or past 110 wins.

Beat the Calculator

A "Calculator" (a player who uses a calculator to solve the problem) and a "Brain" (a player who solves the problem without a calculator) race to see who will be first to solve addition problems.

Use with Lesson 8.10.

Do-Anytime Activities

To work with your child on concepts taught in this unit and in previous units, try these interesting and rewarding activities:

1 Ask questions, such as the following: *What is the fraction word for each of 4 equal parts of something?* (fourths) *Each of eight equal parts?* (eighths)

2 Give your child several pieces of paper to fold into halves, fourths, or eighths. He or she can label each part with the appropriate fraction symbol ($\frac{1}{2}$, $\frac{1}{4}$, $\frac{1}{8}$).

3 Using a set of numbers, have your child write the largest and smallest 2- and 3-digit whole numbers possible. For example, using 5, 2, and 9, the largest whole number is 952; the smallest is 259.

4 Say a 2- or 3-digit number. Then have your child identify the actual value of the digit in each place. For example, in the number 952, the value of the 9 is 900, the value of the 5 is 50, and the value of the 2 is 2 ones, or two. An important goal of *Everyday Mathematics* is for children eventually to think of any digit in a multidigit number by its place-value name.

Use with Lesson 8.10.

215

As You Help Your Child with Homework

As your child brings home assignments, you may want to go over the instructions together, clarifying them as necessary. The answers listed below will guide you through this unit's Home Links.

Home Link 9.2

1. 41	**2.** 71	**3.** 23
4. 72	**5.** 78	**6.** 66
7. 65	**8.** 79	**9.** 38
10. 34	**11.** 21	**12.** 93

Home Link 9.3

1.
```
43
53
63
73
83
```

2.
```
23 24 25
33
   43
   53
   63 64
      73
```

3.
```
      59
      69
78 79 80
88 89 90
```

4.
```
22
32
   43
   53
      64
      74
```

5.
```
53      55
      64
   73   75
```

Home Link 9.4

1. |||||||........ 77

2. ||||| 58

3. 71   **4.** 75   **5.** 59

Home Link 9.6

1. $\frac{1}{5}$ **2.** $\frac{2}{3}$ **3.** $\frac{5}{6}$

4.   **5.**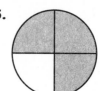

6.

Home Link 9.7

2. $\frac{1}{3}$ **3.** $\frac{1}{4}$ **4.** $\frac{5}{8}$

Home Link 9.8

1.   **2.**

3.

4. hexagon, square
5. 2
6. 3 pennies

Use with Lesson 8.10.

Number-Grid Hunt

Family Note

Ask your child to describe some of the patterns in the number grid below. Then ask him or her to fill in specific numbers you suggest. For example: where would the number 140 go? Do this with a few other numbers before your child completes the rest of the grid. By learning to identify and use patterns in the number grid, your child will develop a strong number sense as well as computation skills.

Please return this Home Link to school tomorrow.

Ask someone to say a number. Record it on the number grid. Do this for several numbers. Then finish filling in the grid on your own.

101									
			125						
							139		
									150
171									
	183								

Using the Number Grid

Family Note

Ask your child to explain how to count up and back by 10s on the number grid and then to demonstrate how to solve the addition and subtraction problems on the number grid. If your child counts one space at a time, remind him or her that to count up by 10s, you can move down one row for every 10 and to count back by 10s, you can move up one row for every 10.

Please return this Home Link to school tomorrow.

Use the number grid to solve the problems.

									0
1	2	3	4	5	6	7	8	9	10
11	12	13	14	15	16	17	18	19	20
21	22	23	24	25	26	27	28	29	30
31	32	33	34	35	36	37	38	39	40
41	42	43	44	45	46	47	48	49	50
51	52	53	54	55	56	57	58	59	60
61	62	63	64	65	66	67	68	69	70
71	72	73	74	75	76	77	78	79	80
81	82	83	84	85	86	87	88	89	90
91	92	93	94	95	96	97	98	99	100

1. $35 + 6 =$ ＿＿＿

2. $61 + 10 =$ ＿＿＿

3. $43 - 20 =$ ＿＿＿

4. ＿＿＿ $= 82 - 10$ **5.** ＿＿＿ $= 58 + 20$ **6.** ＿＿＿ $= 75 - 9$

7. $\begin{array}{r} 55 \\ + 10 \\ \hline \end{array}$ **8.** $\begin{array}{r} 99 \\ - 20 \\ \hline \end{array}$ **9.** $\begin{array}{r} 46 \\ - 8 \\ \hline \end{array}$

Challenge

10. $\begin{array}{r} 84 \\ - 50 \\ \hline \end{array}$ **11.** $\begin{array}{r} 39 \\ - 18 \\ \hline \end{array}$ **12.** ＿＿＿ $= 62 + 31$

Number-Grid Puzzles

Family Note

Have your child show you how to complete the number-grid pieces. Encourage him or her to explain patterns in the number grid that are helpful for solving the problems. For example if you move up one row, the digit in the 10s place is 1 less.

Please return this Home Link to school tomorrow.

Show someone at home how to fill in the missing numbers.

1.

53

2.

23		
43

3.

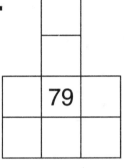

Challenge

4.

22

5.

	2	3	4	5	6	7	8	9	0
1	2	3	4	5	6	7	8	9	10
11	12	13	14	15	16	17	18	19	20
21	22	23	24	25	26	27	28	29	30
31	32	33	34	35	36	37	38	39	40
41	42	43	44	45	46	47	48	49	50
51	52	53	54	55	56	57	58	59	60
61	62	63	64	65	66	67	68	69	70
71	72	73	74	75	76	77	78	79	80
81	82	83	84	85	86	87	88	89	90
91	92	93	94	95	96	97	98	99	100

Solving Problems Two Ways

Family Note

Ask your child to explain how to solve the first set of problems with base-10 blocks and the second set on the number grid. Please do not teach your child a formal algorithm for addition, as shown in margin. It is important that children at this stage work with more concrete representations. This will be beneficial later on, when they are faced with more difficult problems.

Please return this Home Link to school tomorrow.

$$
\begin{array}{r}
52 \\
+\ 35 \\
\hline
87
\end{array}
$$

Show the total number of base-10 blocks. Then write the total.

Example ||||.. + |||..... = ||||||||.......

52   +   35   =   87

1. |..... + ||||||.. =

15   +   62   =   ____

2. |||.... + ||.... =

34   +   24   =   ____

Use the number grid to help you solve the problems.

3. 63 + 8 = ____

4. 55 + 20 = ____

5. ____ = 47 + 12

									0
1	2	3	4	5	6	7	8	9	10
11	12	13	14	15	16	17	18	19	20
21	22	23	24	25	26	27	28	29	30
31	32	33	34	35	36	37	38	39	40
41	42	43	44	45	46	47	48	49	50
51	52	53	54	55	56	57	58	59	60
61	62	63	64	65	66	67	68	69	70
71	72	73	74	75	76	77	78	79	80
81	82	83	84	85	86	87	88	89	90
91	92	93	94	95	96	97	98	99	100

Family Note

In class today, children used blocks to make the mirror image of a design across a line of symmetry. This resulted in a symmetrical design. A figure is symmetrical across a line if it has two matching halves. On this page, help your child complete the designs so that they are symmetrical.

Please return this Home Link to school tomorrow.

Complete each design so the two halves will match.

Example

1.

2.

3.

4.

5.

6. Which completed design shows a letter of the alphabet?

7. Draw a design of your own on one side of a line. Complete the design on the other side of the line. When you fold on the line the two halves should match. Use the back of this page.

Fractional Parts

Family Note

In Unit 8, we worked with unit fractions, such as $\frac{1}{2}$, $\frac{1}{3}$, and $\frac{1}{4}$. Today, we started to explore fractions in which the number above the fraction bar is more than 1, such as $\frac{2}{3}$, $\frac{3}{4}$, and $\frac{5}{6}$. If your child is having trouble with some of the problems on this page, you might mention that $\frac{1}{2}$ means that 1 out of 2 parts is shaded, that $\frac{3}{6}$ means that 3 out of 6 parts are shaded, and so on. Or you might ask your child to explain the fractions to you in this way.

Please return this Home Link to school tomorrow.

Mark the fraction that tells what part of the circle is shaded.

1.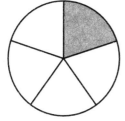

$\frac{1}{2}$ $\frac{5}{6}$

$\frac{1}{5}$ $\frac{5}{1}$

2.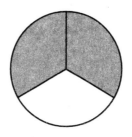

$\frac{2}{2}$ $\frac{2}{3}$

$\frac{3}{4}$ $\frac{3}{1}$

3.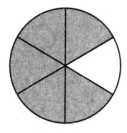

$\frac{1}{6}$ $\frac{1}{5}$

$\frac{6}{5}$ $\frac{5}{6}$

Shade the circles.

4.

Shade $\frac{4}{6}$.

5.

Shade $\frac{3}{4}$.

6.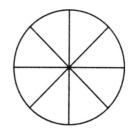

Shade $\frac{5}{8}$.

Challenge

7. Find 2 circles on this page that have the same fraction of the whole shaded. Mark them with an X.

Comparing Fractions

Family Note

Today we divided unit strips into equal parts: halves, thirds, fourths, sixths, and eighths. Then we compared the sizes of the parts. Your child probably cannot tell which of two fractions is more by looking at the fractions, but he or she should be able to compare two fractions by looking at pictures of them. Encourage your child to label one part of each shape with a fraction before deciding which fraction is more or less.

Please return this Home Link to school tomorrow.

1. Which would you rather have, half of candy bar A or half of candy bar B? Explain your answer to someone at home.

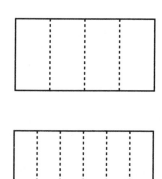

2. Which is more, $\frac{1}{5}$ or $\frac{1}{3}$?

3. Which is more, $\frac{1}{4}$ or $\frac{1}{6}$?

Challenge

4. Which is less, $\frac{3}{4}$ or $\frac{5}{8}$?

Solving Fraction Problems

 Family Note

This Home Link reviews some of the fraction concepts we have covered this year. The most important concept first graders should understand is that a fraction names a part of something (the whole) that has been divided into equal parts. Because for many children the work this year is a first exposure to fraction concepts, they may still be unclear about some of the ideas we have explored. That's okay; these and other fraction concepts will be revisited in later grades.

Please return this Home Link to school tomorrow.

1. Shade $\frac{1}{4}$ of the circle.

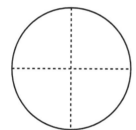

2. Shade $\frac{2}{3}$ of the hexagon.

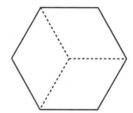

3. Shade $\frac{5}{8}$ of the square.

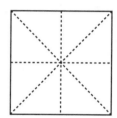

4. Circle the names of the shapes for which you shaded more than $\frac{1}{2}$ of the shape.

circle   hexagon   square

5. Divide the rectangle into fourths.
Shade $\frac{1}{2}$ of the rectangle.
How many fourths did you shade? _____

6. Four friends share 12 pennies equally.
Circle the number of pennies that each friend gets.

Unit 10: **End-of-Year Reviews and Assessments**

In Unit 10, children will review the concepts and skills they have learned throughout the year. Children will review ways to make sense of collections of data, such as height measurements. Specifically, they will use the data they collected at the beginning of the year to calculate how much they have grown during the last few months.

Children will also continue to use mental math strategies to solve number stories involving money.

Finally, children will review the following skills:

· Telling time to 5 minutes on an analog clock

· Using straws to construct geometric figures

· Reading and comparing temperatures on a thermometer

· Understanding place-value concepts

· Using the number grid

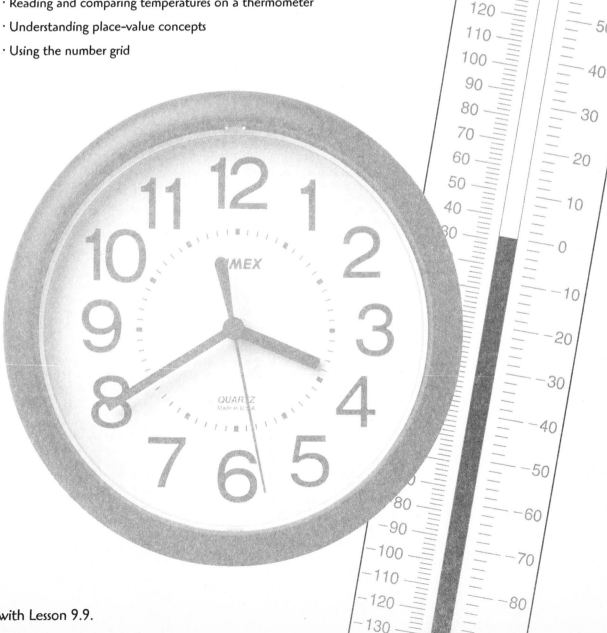

Do-Anytime Activities

To work with your child on the concepts reviewed in this unit, try these interesting and rewarding activities:

1 Continue to work on telling time to the minute.

2 Ask for answers to number stories that involve two or more items. *For example:* I want to buy a donut for 45 cents and a juice box for 89 cents. How much money do I need? ($1.34) Encourage your child to use mental math, coins, the number line, or the number grid to work out solutions.

3 Point to a 3-digit number, such as 528. Ask what the digit "2" means (20); the "5" (500); the "8" (8).

4 Have your child create the largest and smallest numbers given 3 digits.

5 Together, note the thermometer temperature when the weather feels too hot, too cold, or about right. Encourage your child to read any temperature sign or billboard when you travel, noting whether the degrees are Celsius or Fahrenheit.

Building Skills through Games

In this unit, your child will practice addition and money skills by playing the following games:

Beat the Calculator

A "Calculator" (a player who uses a calculator to solve the problem) and a "Brain" (a player who solves the problem without a calculator) race to see who will be first to solve addition problems.

Buyer and Vendor Game

Players take turns being the "Buyer" and the "Vending Machine." The "Buyer" gives the "Vending Machine" the correct amount in coins for the purchase of an item. The "Vending Machine" determines if the coin combination is correct.

As You Help Your Child with Homework

As your child brings home assignments, you may want to go over the instructions together, clarifying them as necessary. The answers listed below will guide you through this unit's Home Links.

Home Link 10.2

3. 15   **4.** 30   **5.** 15   **6.** 20

Home Link 10.3

1. 95¢, or $0.95   **2.** $1.00

Home Link 10.4

1. 15¢   **2.** 20¢

3. 90¢; 10¢   **4.** $1.20; 80¢

Home Link 10.5

1. pentagon   **2.** rectangle   **3.** octagon

4. hexagon   **5.** square   **6.** triangle

Home Link 10.6

1. 48°F   **2.** 72°F   **3.** 47°F

4. 59°F   **5.** 65°F   **6.** 20°F

Graphing Birth Months

Family Note

Today your child figured out about how many inches he or she has grown in the last few months. We collected height information for the whole class and graphed it. We also found the typical height and the typical growth of the children in the class. Help your child graph the months in which his or her friends and family members were born. For each person, your child should color one box above the birth month.

Please return this Home Link to school tomorrow.

Birth Months of Friends and Family Members

Jan. Feb. Mar. Apr. May June July Aug. Sept. Oct. Nov. Dec.

1. From how many people
did you collect information? _____

2. Which month had more
births than any of the others? _____

3. How many births were there in that month? _____

4. Which month had the fewest number of births? _____

5. How many births were there in that month? _____

Telling Time

Family Note

Today, we reviewed how to tell time to the nearest half-hour, quarter-hour, and five minutes. We also set our clocks to a time and then counted the minutes to a later time. Help your child answer the questions below. Use the paper clock your child brought home earlier this year or use a watch or clock on which you can easily see the minute marks and move the hands.

Please return this Home Link to school tomorrow.

Have someone at home help you find a clock or watch that you can use to set the hands to practice telling time.

1. Ask that person to give you a time. Set the hands of the clock to show the time. Do a few more problems like this one.

2. Ask the person to show a time on the clock. You say the time and write it the way it looks on a digital clock. Do a few more problems like this one.

Try these problems.

3. Set the clock to 2 o'clock.
   How many more minutes until quarter-past 2? ____ minutes

4. Set the clock to 4:15.
   How many more minutes until quarter-to 5? ____ minutes

5. Set the clock to 6:45.
   How many more minutes until 7:00? ____ minutes

6. Set the clock to 7:10.
   How many more minutes until 7:30? ____ minutes

Solving Number Stories

Family Note

Ask your child to explain what he or she did to solve Problems 1 and 2 below. Your child may want to act out the problems with coins. If you use an ad for Problem 3, help your child choose an appropriate example (all prices should be less than $1). Ask for an explanation of the solution.

Please return this Home Link to school tomorrow.

For each problem, use Ⓟ, Ⓝ, Ⓓ, Ⓠ, or ⎡$1⎤ to show the amount you pay.

1. You want to buy a and a .

How much will you pay? _____

2. You want to buy a and a .

How much will you pay? _____

Show the amount in two different ways.

3. Make up a number story and solve it. Use the pictures above. Or, find an ad and tape it to the back of this page.

Comparing Costs

Family Note

Ask your child to explain how he or she solved the problems on this page. Encourage your child to act out the problems with coins, draw pictures of base-10 blocks, or count on a number grid.

Please return this Home Link to school tomorrow.

1. A costs how much more than a ? _____

2. You buy a . You pay with Ⓠ Ⓠ Ⓠ.

How much change will you get? _____

3. You buy a and .

How much will you pay? _____

You pay with $1. How much change will you get? _____

Challenge

4. You buy a and a .

How much will you pay? _____

You pay with ⎡$1⎤ ⎡$1⎤. How much change will you get? _____ ¢. Use Ⓟ, Ⓝ, Ⓓ, Ⓠ, or ⎡$1⎤. Show this amount on the back of this page.

Geometry Review

Family Note

Today we reviewed several ideas about polygons and 3-dimensional shapes. Ask your child to point out objects of various shapes around the house or outside.

Please return this Home Link to school tomorrow.

Word Bank		
hexagon	octagon	pentagon
rectangle	square	triangle

Write the name of each shape under the shape.

1.

2.

3.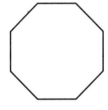

_____ _____ _____

4. I have 6 sides and 6 corners. What am I? _____

5. I am a special rectangle. All of my sides are equal.

What am I? _____

6. I have the smallest number of corners of all the shapes listed in the Word Bank. What am I? _____

7. Make up your own riddle on the back of this page.

Comparing Temperatures

Family Note

The focus of this Home Link is on finding how much warmer or colder one temperature is than another. Ask your child to explain how he or she solved each problem. One strategy might be to count on the thermometer or on a number grid. Your child might even be able to solve some of the problems mentally.

Please return this Home Link to school tomorrow.

°F
120
110

Body   100
Temperature
90

80

Room → 70
Temperature

60

50

40

Water →
Freezes   30

20

10

0

−10

−20

−30

−40

1. Which temperature is
10°F warmer than 38°F? _____°F

2. Which temperature is
20°F warmer than 52°F? _____°F

3. Which temperature is
40°F colder than 87°F? _____°F

4. Which temperature is
20°F colder than 79°F? _____°F

5. Which temperature is
15°F warmer than 50°F? _____°F

6. Which temperature is
25°F colder than 45°F? _____°F

Make up some of your own
temperature comparisons.

Congratulations!

By completing *First Grade Everyday Mathematics* your child has accomplished a great deal. Thank you for all of your support!

This Family Letter is provided for you to use as a resource throughout your child's vacation. It includes a special list of Do-Anytime Activities, game directions, an Addition/Subtraction Facts Table, and a sneak preview of what your child will be learning in *Second Grade Everyday Mathematics*.

Enjoy your vacation!

Do-Anytime Activities

To help your child review many of the things he or she has learned in first grade, we suggest the following activities for you and your child to do together over vacation. These activities will help your child build on the skills he or she has learned this year and help prepare him or her for *Second Grade Everyday Mathematics*.

Telling Time and Using Money

· Practice telling time by using a variety of clocks—billboard clocks, wristwatches, clocks with hands, and digital clocks—in a variety of situations.

· Set alarm clocks and timers on ovens, microwave ovens, and VCRs.

· Record the time spent doing various activities.

· Use real money in a variety of situations: allowance, savings, purchases (including getting change back), and using vending machines.

Weather Watch

· Invite your child to share your interest in weather predictions and temperature reports from the radio, the television, and local and national newspapers.

· Observe temperatures shown on billboards, aquarium thermometers, and so on.

· Read and set temperatures on heating and cooling thermostats and oven dials.

Beginning Geometry

· Look for geometric shapes in the real world, such as street signs, boxes, cans, construction cones, and so on.

· Construct polygons (2–dimensional shapes) out of drinking straws and twist-ties from plastic storage bags. Small-diameter straws are easier to work with and are easily cut into 4–inch or 6–inch lengths. If only large-diameter straws are available, fold back the ends of the twist ties for a tighter fit. To build the polygons, put 2 twist-ties (or 1 folded twist-tie) into one end of each straw, so that each end can be connected to two other straws.

· Construct 3-dimensional figures out of straws and twist-ties. (It helps to connect the base straws first.)

Continuing with Scrolls and Number-Grid Puzzles

· Have your child fill in blank number grids and tape them together in order. Doing this will help your child see two basic patterns of our base-ten numeration system:

   1. By using one or more of the digits 0 through 9, any positive number can be written.

   2. There is no end to counting numbers—there is always at least one more, no matter how far you count.

Here are two problem-solving challenges:

· Have your child fill in the cells on a piece of a grid to create letters of the alphabet, patterns, and designs.

· Create puzzles from pieces of grids in which most of the numbers are missing.

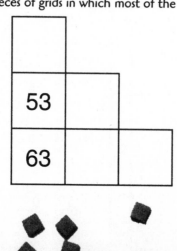

Use with Lesson 10.7.

Fact Power and Games

Knowing basic addition and subtraction facts is as important in learning mathematics as knowing words by sight is in learning to read. Games are a fun way to provide the frequent practice children need in order to gain fact power, or the ability to automatically recall basic addition and subtraction facts. Children will build on their fact power in second grade; especially as they move on to computational skills with multidigit numbers.

The following section lists rules for several games that can be played at home. The number cards used in some games can be made from 3" by 5" index cards or from a regular playing-card deck. Cutout dominoes can also be used in place of number cards.

Addition Top-It

Materials ❏ number cards 0–20 (2 sets)

Players 2 or more

Directions

Players combine and shuffle their cards and place them in a pile, facedown. Each player takes 2 cards from the top of the pile and says the sum of the numbers. The player with the greater sum takes all of the cards then in play. The player with the most cards is the winner. Ties are broken by drawing again—winner takes all.

Beat the Calculator

Materials ❏ number cards 0–10 (4 of each)

❏ calculator

Players 3 (a "Caller," a "Calculator," and a "Brain.")

Directions

Shuffle the cards and place the deck facedown. The Caller turns over the top two cards. The Calculator finds the sum of the numbers on the cards by using a calculator. The Brain solves the problem without a calculator. The Caller determines who got the correct answer first. Players trade roles.

Penny Grab

Materials 20 or more pennies; paper and pencil

Players 2 or more

Directions

Each player grabs a handful of pennies, counts, and records the amount with cents and dollars-and-cents notation. For example, 13 pennies would be recorded as both 13¢ and $0.13. Partners compare their amounts and then figure out and record how many in all (the sum). Players repeat the grabs several times.

Variation: Use nickels or dimes

High Roller

Materials 2 dice

Players 2 or more

Directions

One player rolls 2 dice. The player keeps the die with the larger number (the High Roller) and throws the other die again. The player then counts on from the number rolled on the first die to get the sum of the two dice.

Use with Lesson 10.7.

Addition/subtraction fact families can also be practiced on the Addition/Subtraction Facts Table. This table can be used to keep a record of facts that have been learned.

+, −	0	1	2	3	4	5	6	7	8	9
0	0	1	2	3	4	5	6	7	8	9
1	1	2	3	4	5	6	7	8	9	10
2	2	3	4	5	6	7	8	9	10	11
3	3	4	5	6	7	8	9	10	11	12
4	4	5	6	7	8	9	10	11	12	13
5	5	6	7	8	9	10	11	12	13	14
6	6	7	8	9	10	11	12	13	14	15
7	7	8	9	10	11	12	13	14	15	16
8	8	9	10	11	12	13	14	15	16	17
9	9	10	11	12	13	14	15	16	17	18

Looking Ahead: Second Grade Everyday Mathematics

Next year, your child will ...

· Explore multiplication and division

· Use/arrays, diagrams, and pictures to solve multiplication and division number stories

· Read and write 5-digit numbers

· Compare fractions

· Find the range and median of a set of data

· Classify 2- and 3-dimensional shapes

· Use tools to measure length, area, weight, capacity, and volume

Again, thank you for all of your support this year. Have fun continuing your child's mathematics experiences throughout the vacation!